Inside the Sinclair QL

An introductory guide to the hardware

Jeff Naylor & Diane Rogers

D1614711

First published 1985 by:
Sunshine Books (an imprint of Scot Books Ltd.)
12–13 Little Newport Street
London WC2H 7PP

British Library Cataloguing in Publication Data
Naylor, Jeff
    Inside the Sinclair QL.
    1. Sinclair QL (Computer)
    I. Title   II. Rogers, Diane
    001.64′04   QA76.8.S625

    ISBN 0-946408-40-8

Cover design by Grad Graphic Design Ltd.
Illustration by Stuart Hughes.
Typeset by Paragon Photoset, Aylesbury.
Printed in England by Short Run Press Ltd, Exeter.

CONTENTS

Contents in detail

CHAPTER 4
The Processor at Work
The contents of the central processing unit, internal buses, registers, program counter, stack pointer, data register, address register, status register, flags, instruction register, arithmetic and logic unit, the control unit — what happens inside the central processing unit, fetching data from memory, incrementing the program counter — how the central processing unit obeys programs, machine code, instructions sets, mnemonics, running a program, starting the program, sequential programming — common machine code operations, moving data, addressing modes, arithmetic and logic, jumping about, stacking data.

CHAPTER 5
Introducing the QL
History of the Sinclair QL — QL specifications — hardware structure, the 68008, the 8049, the custom chip, the ZX8302, crystals, ROM chips, RAM chips, taking your machine apart.

CHAPTER 6
At the Heart of the QL: the 68008
External connections, supply connections, data bus, address bus, control bus, asynchronous bus control, synchronous bus control, bus arbitration, interrupt pins, signalling the state of the CPU, system control — inside the 68008, data registers, address registers, stack pointers, status register — processing states — operating modes, supervisor and user modes, privileged instructions — exceptions — interrupts.

CHAPTER 7
Talking to the CPU: the 68008 Instruction Set
An alphabetical listing of the instruction set, as a reference section.

CHAPTER 8
Exploring Machine Code
Demonstrating some simple machine code routines — Machine Code Demo program, RESPR, POKE_W, CALL — Custom Error Messages program — Monitor program.

CHAPTER 9
The Memory Map
The allocation of the memory addresses — physical memory map, QDOS routines and SuperBASIC interpreter, ROM, expansion areas, I/O, RAM — software memory map, system variables, the heap, RESPR, transient program area, SuperBASIC program area.

CHAPTER 10
The Video Display
The ZX8302, the master chip or video chip — controlling the ZX8302, avoiding clashes with the CPU, the second screen — the screen display, high resolution, low resolution, printing characters, user-definable characters, User Defined Shapes program.

CHAPTER 11
Input and Output
The 8049 processor, the IPC — the keyboard, how the keys work — the CTL sockets — sound — RS232 and networks, baud, handshaking — microdrives.

CHAPTER 12
Software Maketh the Machine
SuperBASIC, programming — QDOS, calling QDOS routines — traps, manager routines, trap 1, trap 2, trap 3 — vectors.

SECTION 1
General Principles

CHAPTER 1
Fundamental Principles

Electronics of the digital kind

You have probably discovered that the apparently inscrutable performance of modern computers is achieved by using 'digital electronics'. Do not be panicked into assuming that this will make computers any harder to understand than a conventional electronic device such as a radio.

If you have tried to understand electronics at some time in the past, and struggled to comprehend such things as sine waves, modulation and capacitance, then take heart — the theory behind digital techniques requires less in the way of abstract concepts or knowledge of mathematics. It is the size (a great deal crammed into a small package) and speed of operation that make modern computers so powerful.

So what is the difference between digital electronics and the more conventional kind? Broadly speaking, a digital circuit is only concerned with the presence or absence of electricity — in other words, whether parts of itself are ON or OFF. The exact amount of electricity present, provided it falls within certain limits, is unimportant. Conventional circuits ('analogue' circuits) tend to be much more precise. For example, in a hi-fi system the quantities of electricity flowing out to the loudspeakers reflect exactly the changing levels of sound that the circuit is trying to imitate: in a badly designed system, the levels of electricity may not be controlled accurately enough, resulting in distortion.

Charles Babbage is sometimes known as the father of modern computing because he designed the first 'Analytic Engine' in the 1830s. It was indeed an engine, with plungers, levers and cogs interacting in a visible, tangible way.

Understanding the behaviour of a mechanical device is easier on the brain because there is nothing abstract to comprehend — pulling this lever operates that plunger because they are attached to each other by a wire which we can see. In order to come to terms with an electronic device, it is common to envisage a picture of electricity behaving like water, or even little people rushing around. There is nothing to be ashamed of in using these analogies, but they are not accurate enough to cope with complex models: a circuit consisting of a battery, bulb and switch can be resolved in these terms, but try to apply your analogy to a television set and you may misunderstand how it works.

The nature of electricity

In order to have a picture of the nature of electricity, it is first necessary to appreciate a few simple facts about matter. All of these facts would take some time to prove, so I won't attempt to do that here: besides, in the final analysis you would still have to take my word for it, just as I am taking someone else's.

Let us, therefore, accept that matter, whether it is a solid, a liquid or a gas, is made up of extremely small particles called 'atoms' — a simple definition of an atom is 'the smallest particle that can exist'.

There are well over a hundred types of atom, and some are more common than others. Materials which consist of only one type of atom are called 'elements': these include such familiar substances as carbon, iron and oxygen. The atoms of one element differ from those of another by their size and structure, varying from the simple hydrogen atom to heavyweights such as uranium. Other substances consist of different types of atom grouped together, sometimes as a simple mixture of elements, but often as the result of the atoms bonding together and forming what is known as a 'molecule'. For example, two atoms of hydrogen locked together with one atom of oxygen make up a molecule of water.

Over a period of some time, scientists have established a picture of what makes up an atom and it is in the construction of each type of atom that the key to electricity lies. An atom consists of a nucleus of a number of 'protons' and 'neutrons'. This nucleus is the so-called 'indivisible core', the prising open of which leads to the science of particle physics. Around this core orbit 'electrons'. Each type of atom has a different requirement of electrons to make them ideally balanced: hydrogen has only one, whilst others can have dozens. However, some atoms can sustain a small imbalance in their construction, and either host additional electrons or relinquish some of their normal quota. As their name implies, the electrons are responsible for all electrical phenomena.

If we consider the behaviour of electrons in a battery, an environment which is easy to visualise, we can begin to understand how electricity can be made to be useful. Batteries are constructed in such a way as to be a source of electricity by containing two areas, one with a surplus of electrons, and the other with a deficiency. Some batteries, such as those found in cars, can be recharged when the imbalance between the two areas has equalled out; others, such as torch cells, contain chemicals which cannot easily be rejuvenated.

The two areas are connected to terminals on the outside of the case. The terminal attached to the area containing the surplus of electrons is called the 'negative' terminal, and it is marked with a minus sign. At first glance this may seem illogical but, as this is how the early experimenters labelled their batteries, the tradition is too well established to be tampered with now. This negative terminal is the jumping-off point for the electrons, which are eager to get across to the other terminal, marked with a plus sign and called 'positive'.

You are probably aware that one of the units used in the measurement of electricity is the 'volt': this can be thought of as the pressure on the electrons to move away from their present, overcrowded, host atoms to find a more welcoming home. Electrons and the nucleus of atoms behave in a similar way to magnets. The north pole of a magnet is attracted to the south pole of another, and vice versa, whilst two north (or two south) poles have the reverse effect, actually repelling each other. Electrons don't like other electrons to be present, so if an atom is hosting too many electrons these tend to put pressure on each other to go away: if the opportunity occurs (ie if they can move to an atom with too few electrons), the surplus tend to leave.

Do not think of voltage as the number of spare electrons. The latter is an indication of the capacity of the battery, and therefore relates to how long that battery would keep working: voltage is the force with which an electron is trying to escape.

It is now time to look at a circuit. You should recognise the components in **Figure 1.1**. **Figure 1.2** is the same thing drawn as a circuit diagram, using symbols to make the drawing easier and the overall picture simpler to understand, once you know what the symbols are meant to represent.

As you can see, the battery is connected to the other parts of the circuit by wire — electrons cannot travel through air unless the voltage is very high, as in the case of lightning. Some materials allow the relatively easy

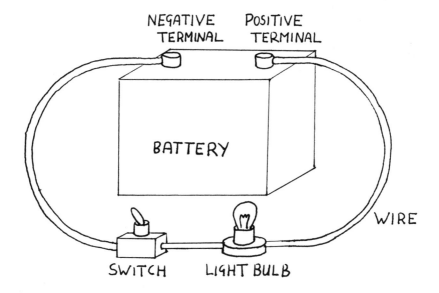

Figure 1.1: A Simple Circuit

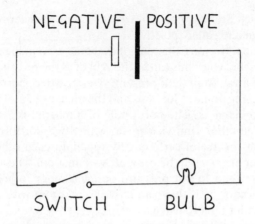

NEGATIVE | POSITIVE

SWITCH   BULB

Figure 1.2: Circuit Diagram

movement of free electrons and are said to be 'conductive': if a substance only allows the flow grudgingly, causing the electrons to work hard for their passage, then it is called 'resistive'.

In fact, all conductors have some resistance, but in the case of a connecting wire made of metal (probably copper) the resistance is so small as to be irrelevant. A light bulb contains a particular type of wire, known as the 'filament', which has sufficient resistance to ensure that the electrons, jostling past the atoms of the filament, cause it to heat up until it glows and gives off light. In order to prevent the wire burning up, it is encased in a glass bubble which is filled with inert gases so that the filament has nothing with which to react. It is the amount of flow through the bulb which determines how much light the filament gives off: this flow is called 'current' and we measure it in 'amps'.

The final component in the figures is the switch, the operation of which is accurately expressed by its symbol. The switch provides a mechanical gap in the conductor which can be made good when the switch is closed; when it is open, the entire voltage difference of the circuit is present between its two contacts.

Figure 1.3 shows what happens when the switch is closed. The voltage present causes electrons to travel along the wire, through the now closed switch, until they reach the bottleneck caused by the resistive nature of the bulb's filament. After passing through the filament, the electrons are on the home straight and finally they arrive at their goal, the positive terminal of the battery, where they find an atom which is not overcrowded, around which they can orbit.

By now you should have a picture of how the electric circuit in a torch behaves. Perhaps you may like to compare it with a simple water analogy, which at this level of complexity holds true.

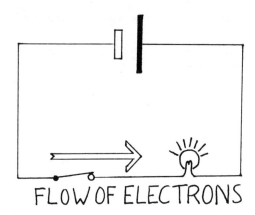

FLOW OF ELECTRONS

Figure 1.3: A Completed Circuit

The negative terminal of the battery can be thought of as a tank of water stored in a loft. Voltage relates to the height of the tank and therefore to the pressure that is trying to force the water through the pipes. The amount of water in the tank is the capacity of the battery. If there is a stopcock, this will act like a switch, cutting off the flow. Any narrow pieces of pipe would restrict the flow in the same manner as a bulb limits current.

You will be able to see that the three variables (or 'parameters') of our simple circuit — voltage, current and resistance — are related to each other. Connect a bulb with a higher resistance into the circuit and the flow of current will be smaller; use a battery with a higher voltage and the flow will be greater. Their relationship is fixed in mathematical terms as 'Ohm's Law'. This states that the current in amps flowing through a circuit is equal to the voltage in volts, divided by the resistance of the circuit measured in 'ohms'. This means that we can calculate any one of these values if we know the other two. Although you will not need to perform such maths, I trust that when I use the words voltage, current and resistance, I can safely visualise comprehending faces rather than blank stares.

Digital circuits

Now we can side-step much electrical theory and move on to more practical matters. In glancing through any modern electronics catalogue, you are likely to find a large section devoted to 'digital integrated circuits'. These go under names, such as TTL and CMOS, which do little to promote understanding of their function. (CMOS stands for complementary metal oxide semiconductor, which indicates how it is made rather than what it does: transistor transistor logic is a little more helpful in explaining TTL.) These components are the building blocks of logic circuits — some of them are already prefabricated into fairly complex circuits themselves.

Even the largest computers use the same building blocks — there are simply more of them.

In order to follow the processes involved in a digital circuit, it is necessary to know something about 'semiconductors'. These are substances which do not occur in nature — they are manufactured from highly-refined materials such as germanium and silicon to have particular, very useful, properties.

The simplest device we can build from semiconducting materials is a 'diode', which has two terminals and can pass current in only one direction. Even more useful is the 'transistor', the resistance of which varies when a voltage is applied at a *third* terminal. If we revert to the water analogy, the transistor is like a tap and the voltage present at the third terminal can be thought of as a hand on the tap, controlling the flow. In analogue circuits, the precision of these devices is critical as the amount of flow allowed through the transistor is proportional to the control voltage. In digital circuits, however, each stage in the circuit is only concerned with whether or not there is a voltage present, so the transistors can be less precise in their manufacture — they are only acting as electrically-controlled switches.

I have talked about things being on or off: I should also mention some other terms. If a positive voltage is present, then that part of the circuit is said to be 'high', or at 'logic level 1'. Conversely, the negative parts of the circuit are said to be 'low', or at 'logic level 0'. There is another possibility, which occurs when an area is not connected to either terminal of the voltage supply — this area is then said to be 'floating'.

Logic gates
It will be useful to describe in detail the function of one logic chip, the '7409 quad two input AND gate'. A 'logic gate' is a point in a circuit where a decision is made. Do not assume that there is anything clever about the decision-making process — given the same set of circumstances, the same gate will always behave in the same way.

The 7409 is called an AND gate because it behaves in the following manner — if its first input is high AND its second input is also high, then the output will be high. The 7409 contains four such gates (hence the 'quad' in its name) and each gate has two input terminals and one output terminal. The chip has 14 pins connecting it to the outside world: four sets of three pins as access to the gates, and two pins for the voltage supply. The 74 series runs on a 5 volt positive supply, the negative terminal being called 'ground', or GND for short. You may be wondering why there are four gates in one package — simply, the cost is so low that the manufacturers might as well make the most of the space.

A useful technique in the study of logic is the drawing up of a truth table. This is a method of assessing how a logic circuit operates and it is worthwhile making use of a simple table in order to define the operation of an AND gate.

Take a look at **Table 1.1**. Across the top of the table are the possible states of input one of an AND gate, and down the side those of input two. Follow the 'input one low' row down to where it crosses the 'input two low' column and you read 'low' — the state of the output when both inputs are low. Now study **Table 1.2**. This describes the behaviour of an OR gate (where the output is high if either input one OR input two is high).

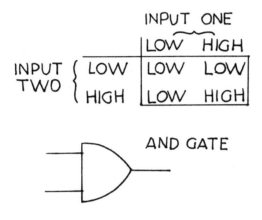

Table 1.1: AND Gate

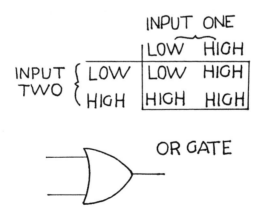

Table 1.2: OR Gate

With **Tables 1.3** and **1.4**, we come across two new words, NAND and NOR. However, these are only AND and OR with an N prefix, which stands for 'not'. If you were to make a truth table for an AND gate but lied each time you wrote an answer, the final result would describe the operation of a NAND gate. One way of achieving this electronically would be by using a circuit called an 'invertor' attached to the output of an AND gate. This is one of the simplest logic devices available as it has only one input and one output: as the name implies, the output is an inverted reflection of its input — it swaps high for low and vice versa. We can also pass the output of an OR gate through an invertor to create a NOR gate.

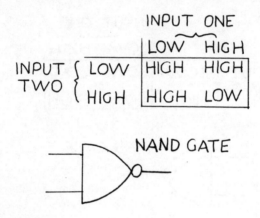

| | | INPUT ONE | |
		LOW	HIGH
INPUT TWO {	LOW	HIGH	HIGH
	HIGH	HIGH	LOW

NAND GATE

Table 1.3: NAND Gate

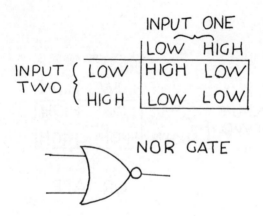

| | | INPUT ONE | |
		LOW	HIGH
INPUT TWO {	LOW	HIGH	LOW
	HIGH	LOW	LOW

NOR GATE

Table 1.4: NOR Gate

One point to bear in mind about the output of all gates is that their voltage is derived from the chip's two supply voltage pins, not the inputs, so the currents flowing through the signal paths of a logic circuit are very low.

Now take a look at **Figure 1.4** — spend a little time working out what will happen when the circuit is turned on, and when the switches are pressed. The diagram represents a latch, or simple 'flip-flop' (this circuit 'latches' on to the last signal sent to it and remembers it). It shows how a pulse, in the form of someone pressing the switch for a moment (ie a logic high being applied briefly to one input of gate one), achieves a permanent result. The circuit consists of two NOR gates, two switches, and two components ('resistors') that greatly impede the flow of current.

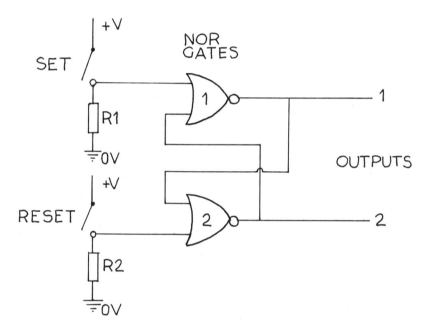

Figure 1.4: A Simple Flip-Flop

Study how the switch and resistor are arranged. If the switch is open, there will be zero volts at the point where the wire leading to one input of the gate is connected to the switch and resistor. Close the switch, and current will flow through the switch and resistor so that the point connected to the gate will be at a high voltage.

Let's follow the operation of the gates. When first connected, and before either switch is closed, assume that both inputs to gate one are at zero volts — check this against the NOR gate truth table and you can see that the result will be a high voltage at the output terminal. The inputs to gate two will be low for the terminal connected to the switch, and high for the one attached to output one, resulting in a low output at output two.

This becomes the second input to gate one, keeps it at a low voltage and so maintains the status quo, ie output one high, output two low.

Now imagine what happens when you close the switch marked SET. The first NOR gate now has a high and a low on its inputs, resulting in a low output. This also affects gate two, which now has two low inputs, so gate two's output goes high. This has an effect on gate one, by making both inputs high, but, as you can see from the truth table, gate one's output remains low. We have a new, but stable, situation with the two output values swapped over.

Now let's see what happens when we reopen the SET switch. Gate one has one low and one high input, so the output remains low. In order to make the outputs flip back, we need to press the RESET switch. Try tracing the logic levels which will result. This circuit could be said to remember which switch was pressed last — if it was SET then output one will be high. Extra circuits can be added to make this device work as a store: as I said before, it can remember a logic level, and this is a property which, as you will see in Chapter 3, is very useful indeed.

Integrated circuits in computers
The simple logic chip containing a number of gates may be the basic building block of computer circuits, but progress has seen the introduction of chips that are much more complex. It stands to reason that if you can build a computer by interconnecting gates, flip-flops, buffers, invertors and other digital components all etched on to their own slices of silicon, a computer can also be constructed by cramming all the components on to *one* slice of silicon. The QL contains a chip like this, the 8049 single chip computer, but this is only used as a 'clever' chip to perform certain input and output operations. All the main types of computer 'integrated circuits' are represented inside the QL, and they are virtually all digital chips: we will meet them individually later in the book.

Some types of chip may employ techniques that are not strictly digital, such as integrated circuits which produce analogue video signals; others may use slightly different electronic techniques internally to achieve certain aims — some memory devices fall into this category. Whatever slight differences may be present inside the integrated circuits of the QL, they can all be thought of as chips with inputs, outputs and requiring voltage supplies. In general, their task is to react to their input with a suitable output — this is rather an over-simplification, but nevertheless true.

Making sounds
Computers often have some means of making a noise, whether this takes the form of simple beeps, music, or complex sound effects to accompany

games. The principles of sound reproduction lead us again into the area of analogue, as opposed to digital, techniques.

First of all, let us examine what the human ear perceives as sound. 'In space, no one can hear you scream' the slogan says, and this is perfectly true — sound travels as vibrations of air molecules. When these vibrations reach our eardrums, they are converted to nerve signals and passed to the brain. Think of how sounds are created — a clap of the hands creates a violent air disturbance, a violin transmits the vibration of its strings to the resonant sound box of its body.

The component most frequently used to convert electrical signals into air vibrations is the loudspeaker. This has a large cone or diaphragm which can stimulate adjacent air molecules. To move the cone itself, the phenomenon of 'electro-magnetism' is exploited: when current passes through a wire, a small local magnetic field is created, and by wrapping the wire into a coil the effect is enhanced. A small permanent magnet is fixed in the vicinity of this coil, and if we pass a current through the coil it will try to move either nearer or further away from the magnet, depending on the direction of the current flow and the polarity of the magnet. This converts the electrical signals into air vibrations. Obviously, loudspeakers vary in quality but, by clever design, highly-accurate sound reproduction is possible.

The simplest form of sound is the 'sine wave', the term for a pure tone or whistle. **Figure 1.5** is a graph of amplitude against time for a loudspeaker reproducing a sine wave. Note that the vertical axis is labelled 'voltage': it could also be labelled 'air pressure' if the speaker were perfect, although due to manufacturing tolerances this is rarely the case. One

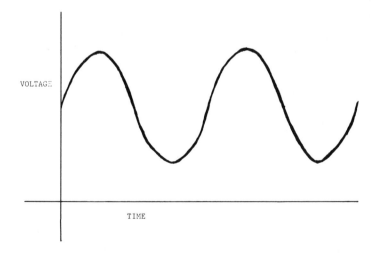

Figure 1.5: A Sine Wave Voltage

cycle of the wave is measured from one peak to the next. Normally, audible frequencies lie in the range of 30 hertz to over 16,000 hertz (one hertz is a cycle per second), depending on how good your ears are.

Musical notes have a fixed mathematical relationship. For example, middle A has a frequency of 440 hertz, and the A an octave above, 880 hertz: therefore, if we know the frequency of a note and want to obtain a note an octave higher, we double the frequency of the original note. (There are 12 semitones in a Western musical scale and each is equal to the frequency of the semitone below multiplied by the twelfth root of two: the twelfth root of two is that number which when multiplied by itself twelve times is equal to two — it is roughly 1.05963.)

We have talked about pure sine wave sounds, but what shape do other sounds take? Most natural sounds are made up of a combination of sine waves, normally with some mathematical relationship. A violin, for instance, will produce a 'fundamental' frequency plus various other related frequencies depending on the construction and quality of its wooden resonant body. The human voice is a complex mixture of waveforms, but the important frequencies lie in the region of 300 to 3000 hertz — most telephone lines have a smaller range than this, but are (normally!) quite intelligible. So you can see that the problems of producing sounds are not insurmountable; with circuits that can produce alternating voltages above 20,000 hertz and sophisticated loudspeaker systems, hi-fi systems are ample proof of this.

Video pictures

The vast majority of personal computers use video screens to communicate back to their users. Whether they use monitors or domestic televisions, the technology developed for broadcast television is employed.

Let us first look at the tube which displays the picture we see — the 'cathode ray tube'. It is represented in cross section by **Figure 1.6**. The air is evacuated from inside the tube and the front face coated with small particles called 'phosphors': at the back of the tube is an 'electron gun'. In the electron gun, a piece of metal called a cathode is heated up, and a high enough voltage is generated between it and the phosphors to cause the electrons at the cathode, already excited by the heat, to travel to the highly attractive positive area that exists at the phosphors. As there is nothing to impede their course, a stream of electrons will flow through the vacuum to their goal.

A magnetic field, and other voltages, can have a marked influence on the path taken by these electrons, so it is possible to use electro-magnetic coils, and extra cathodes and 'anodes' (the positive version of cathodes), in order to deflect and focus the 'beam' of electrons travelling to the phosphors. This beam can be made to arrive at any particular spot on the

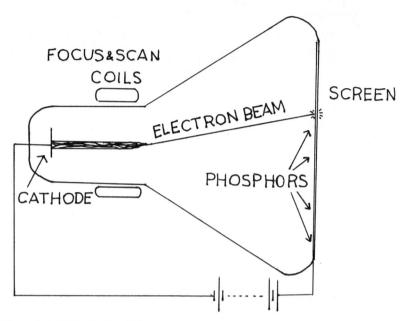

Figure 1.6: Cathode Ray Tube

screen. The special properties of the phosphors are significant. If bombarded with lots of electrons, a phosphor will give a glow of light. Within certain limits, the more electrons, the greater the glow given off — very useful, as we will see in a moment.

So we have a method of lighting up any particular point on the TV screen with the application of suitable control voltages to the various components of the cathode ray tube. It is now a relatively small step to perceive how we might 'paint' a picture by aiming the beam at various parts of the screen and making them glow, moving on to others and returning before the original glow has subsided.

Figure 1.7 shows how this is done. The screen area is divided up into horizontal lines and a line is scanned. The intensity of the beam varies, resulting in the different brightnesses required. The beam is then reduced in intensity as it 'flies back' to the start of the next line, and the process is repeated. When the bottom of the screen has been reached, the beam returns to the top and begins again, but this time it fills in the spaces between the first set of lines. This whole process occurs very quickly, and only a twenty-fifth of a second elapses before the beam returns to the first phosphor it scanned.

In order to make an intelligible picture out of the screen display, its associated circuits must be sent a number of pieces of information. These are pulses which instigate the scanning of a new line or a new 'frame', and voltages that control the brightness generated. The data is contained in an

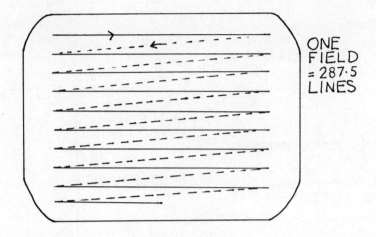

TUBE FACE

Figure 1.7: CRT Screen

analogue signal, called the 'video' signal, which employs negative-going pulses to govern the line and frame circuits: the brightness information is managed by a varying positive voltage coming after the line 'synchronising' pulses (sync pulses for short). **Figure 1.8** is a graph of one line of a video signal. The signals received over the airwaves or from the TV socket of the computer are video signals which have been modulated in the same way as radio signals, so that they can be transmitted and then decoded by the tuner circuits in the television set.

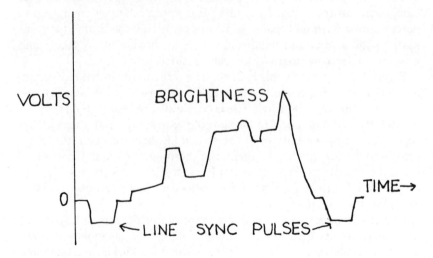

Figure 1.8: Video Signal

Colour makes matters even more complex. Any colour can be made up from a mixture of three very pure sources of 'primary colour' — red, green or blue. A colour television has three kinds of phosphor coated on the screen. The tube contains not one but three electron guns, and masking between the cathodes and the screen ensures that the beam from one gun only lands on one colour of phosphor. The size of the different colour areas is so small that, to the human eye, from a distance, they merge into one source of light. With all three guns set to maximum, the screen will still glow white but, if the relationship of the output of the guns is varied, different colours are displayed. Most colour monitors require the three colour signals to be sent separately and these can achieve a very high quality of display.

Normal televisions expect the colour information to be included in the video signal in what is known as a 'coded composite video' signal, which is then 'modulated' in order to be transmitted. This is how the broadcasting system transmits colour pictures. It means that the channel does not take up any more airspace for colour, and that monochrome receivers can share the same signal. The system used to code the colour information is complex — suffice it to say that colour 'difference' signals are modulated and mixed with the video signal, in much the same way as more than one TV channel can transmit on the airwaves, and a tuner circuit can distinguish between them.

Magnetic recording

The last physical phenomenon that we will examine is that used to make permanent records on tape, microdrive cartridge or disk. As we have seen, a stream of electrons passing along a wire creates a magnetic field. This field is caused by individual electrons: as they are all travelling in one direction, their individual magnetic fields (the ones that make them repel each other) add together to form a larger one. Now think of an atom with a number of electrons in orbit around it — the orbits are of a random nature and therefore the sum effect of the individual electron's magnetism is nil. However, certain materials hold electrons firmly in orbit so, if we can force the electrons to take similar paths, their combined fields will create a magnetic force around the atom.

Iron is by far the most useful magnetic material. It is magnetically 'soft': that is to say, we can alter the orbits of its electrons with little effort, but they can revert back to normal with equal ease. By the addition of chosen impurities at the manufacturing stage, iron can emerge as steel — chemically very similar, but both physically and magnetically harder. So, by careful choice of materials, it is possible to manufacture iron-based substances that can be magnetised and hold their alignment indefinitely.

Recording tape consists of a thin coating of such a magnetic material on a flexible backing. In order to record a signal, we pass the tape over a record head (this is little more than a local electro-magnet which can affect the tape immediately in line with a small gap in its front face). By applying to the head a 'bias' signal (a high frequency alternating voltage that loosens the hold on the electron orbits) along with the signal that we wish to record, magnetic fields are created which reflect the signal. To retrieve the signal from tape, we need only pass it across a replay head (often the record and replay heads are the same device). The magnetic fields from the tape cause currents to flow in the head's electro-magnetic coils, which can be amplified back to the original level of the first signal.

These basic principles apply to all types of magnetic recording. Apart from the quality of the tape itself, there are other factors which affect the performance of any given system. The upper limit of frequencies that may be stored is governed by how small an area of tape the head can view: the smaller the head gap, the less the signal spills over on to adjacent areas of tape. As well as improving the heads, we can increase the speed at which the tape travels past them. In fact, video tape systems move the head diagonally across the tape at high speed, in order to increase the relative tape-to-head speed. Digital data is particularly easy to store magnetically: often only two tones are recorded, one indicating a logic 1, the other a 0.

Magnetic recording formats

Until the introduction of the Sinclair microdrive, personal computers relied on one of two formats to store information, using magnetic techniques. The cheap solution is to press an ordinary audio cassette recorder into service: in this format, the tape inside the cassette is wedged between a pinch wheel and a rotating capstan spindle and dragged past the record/playback head at the rather slow speed of 1⅞ths of an inch per second. The main disadvantages of this system are the slow tape-to-head speed, which means that saving and loading data must be performed at a fairly slow rate, and the linear manner of the recording, which makes finding a particular piece of data a laborious process.

Floppy disk drives employ enclosed disks of magnetic material that are rotated at high speed within the drive. The record/playback head moves across the surface of the disk in steps, recording information on concentric circular tracks. The main drawbacks of cassette tapes are avoided, with high rates of transfer of data and the added bonus that quick access can be gained to any particular section of the disk: a speedy form of random access is therefore possible. The high tolerances required in the manufacture of disk drives make cost their main disadvantage.

The principle of the microdrive owes more to the cassette than the floppy disk. It is described in detail in Chapter 11.

18

CHAPTER 2
Numbers and Data

In the days of the telegraph, communication along the wires was in digital form (using morse code consisting of dots and dashes, rather than ones and zeroes). The process was slow and cumbersome, as the information which was to be sent had to be coded, passed on as a series of dots and dashes, and decoded at the other end of the wire. If only something more complex than a two-state signal could be sent, it would all be a lot quicker: for example, by transmitting 26 uniquely differing signals along the wire, the whole alphabet could be represented.

Analogue and digital techniques would tackle this problem in different ways. An analogue solution might be to vary the length of the dashes, or to place a voltage of changing levels on the line — continue along this path and you will end up with the telephone. The digital solution, however, is to add more lines. If one line can be used to indicate one or zero (on or off), then two lines can indicate any one of four conditions — both lines off, line one on and line two off, line one off and line two on, or both lines on. Three lines can offer eight permutations — the four available from two lines with the third line on or off in each situation.

Imagine a system of communication which consists of *five* wires connecting two devices able to code and decode information. You would be able to have 32 buttons, labelled with letters of the alphabet, for your message. A fairly simple digital circuit could then codify this into a unique five-line signal of ons and offs to transmit to the receiver, which would decode the message and could respond by lighting a particular bulb. This kind of device could, in computer jargon, be called a 'five-bit parallel data transfer system' — that is, a system which passes information ('data') of five 'bits' (ones and zeros or on and off signals) along five wires running in parallel.

Binary and hexadecimal numbers
How people think of numbers depends on their education. I was not introduced to the concept of numbers to a different base until I was too set in my ways to grasp it quickly, but modern maths now teaches early on the idea of numbers to bases other than 10. For those puzzled even by the word 'base', an explanation is required.

We have 10 numbers which only need one figure to represent them — 0 to 9. Each time we want to represent a number which is more than 9, we add to the next column. This is our normal system of counting, the decimal system, and 10 is said to be the base.

But why only 10 figures? If the human race had evolved with 16 fingers and thumbs, we might have had six more single figures to represent the numbers 10 to 15, and then we would have worked to the base 16. Try writing out numbers from 1 to 30, in base 16, using the figures 0 to 9 plus the letters A to F to represent 10 to 15, and compare your results with **Table 2.1**. You are using 'hexadecimal' numbers, a numbering system often favoured by machine code programmers because it is comparatively easy to translate into 'binary' (base 2), which is the way that the computer itself handles numbers.

Table 2.1: Decimal To Hexadecimal Conversion

DEC	HEX	DEC	HEX
0	00	16	10
1	01	32	20
2	02	64	40
3	03	128	80
4	04	256	0100
5	05	512	0200
6	06	1024	0400
7	07	2048	0800
8	08	4096	1000
9	09	8192	2000
10	0A	16384	4000
11	0B	32768	8000
12	0C	65535	FFFF
13	0D		
14	0E		
15	0F		

The computer's method of representing data only permits its columns to contain two figures — 0 and 1. So each time the computer has to represent a number greater than 1, it needs to use more columns. Instead of units, tens, hundreds, thousands and so on (as in decimal), the columns go up in value by the power of 2 (ie 2, 4, 8, 16 etc.).

I have included a program which will help you to explore the relationship between the three bases mentioned, and to allow you to convert values from one base to the others. Although this first program contains no machine code, later ones will do so and you may lose them completely if you run them with a typing error included. In order to prevent this, I strongly recommend that you get into the habit of saving anything that takes you more than 30 seconds to type in, before you run it.

Program 2.1: Binary Demonstration

```
100 REMark      Binary Demonstration
110 MODE 8
120 WINDOW 512,256,0,0
130 BORDER 24,4
140 INK 7:PAPER 1:CLS
150 AT 0,13:PRINT "Data Bus"
160 AT 3,5
170 PRINT"128 64 32 16 8   4   2   1"
180 ARC 20,86 TO 124,86,-.5
190 AT 15,3
200 PRINT "Decimal=",,"Hex="
210 value=0
220 draw_bus
230 REPeat menu
240   AT 17,2
250   PRINT "F1 - calculate  F2 - demonstrate"
260   REPeat get
270     req=KEYROW(0)
280     IF req=2 OR req=8 THEN EXIT get
290   END REPeat get
300   SELect ON req
310   ON req=2
320     REPeat fetch
330       AT 17,2:CLS 3
340       INPUT "value?"!value
350       IF value>-1 AND value<255 THEN EXIT fetch
360     END REPeat fetch
370     draw_bus
380   ON req=8
390     AT 17,2:CLS 3
400     PRINT "F1 for menu, hold F2 to freeze"
410     FOR value=0 TO 255
420       draw_bus
430       REPeat scan
440         IF NOT KEYROW(0) THEN EXIT scan
450         IF KEYROW(0)=2 THEN EXIT value
460       END REPeat scan
470     END FOR value
480   END SELect
490   REPeat wait: IF NOT KEYROW(0) THEN EXIT wait
500 END REPeat menu
510 DEFine PROCedure draw_bus
520   LOCal temp%:temp%=value
530   FOR wire=7 TO 0 STEP -1
540     column=27-wire*3
```

```
550    colour=4-2*(temp% DIV 2^wire)
560    FOR row=4 TO 12
570     AT row,column:PAPER colour
580      PRINT " "
590     END FOR row
600     PAPER 1:AT 13,column
610     PRINT INT(2/colour)
620     temp%=temp% MOD 2^wire
630    END FOR wire
640 AT 15,12:PRINT value;"    "
650 AT 15,29:PRINT hex$(value);"    "
660 END DEFine draw_bus
670 REMark -------------------------
680 DEFine FuNction hex$(a)
690   LOCal h$,t,v
700   h$="":v=a
710   REPeat place
720    t=v-INT(v/16)*16
730    h$=CHR$(t+48+7*(t>9))&h$
740    v=INT(v/16)
750    IF NOT v THEN EXIT place
760   END REPeat place
770   RETurn h$
780   END DEFine hex$
```

Enter Program 2.1 into your computer — you may omit the REM (remark) statements if you wish to save time. When you have saved it, run the program: you will be offered the choice of either a demonstration or a calculation. In the Demonstration mode, the computer will cycle through an eight-bit range of numbers, displaying decimal, binary and hex values, as well as graphically representing a data bus. The eight lines are coloured to indicate their state — green lines are low, or logic 0, red indicates high, or logic 1 (see previous chapter). When using the calculation mode, you may enter a number in any base and the equivalent will be displayed. I suggest that you keep this program handy, or perhaps you might like to simplify it for making quick checks. It is restrictively inflexible to stick to one base at all times.

I mentioned a moment ago that hexadecimal numbers (hex for short) were favoured by machine code programmers because of the relative ease with which they could be translated into binary. The above program helps to demonstrate the relationship between hex and binary (bin for short) — you will notice that an eight-bit binary number can always be expressed as a two-digit hex number, while the lower four bits of a binary value are reflected in a single hex digit. With practice, it is possible mentally to convert binary numbers to hex and vice versa. If you do find hex difficult to come to terms with, then concentrate on understanding binary, as this is vital to the understanding of a digital computer.

Bytes, nibbles, words — the terminology of binary

Values represented in binary are given names, depending on their size.

The QL, together with the majority of home computers, has an eight-bit internal data structure, using eight lines, or binary columns which convey data around the computer. Eight bits can represent numbers in the range 0 to 255 dec, or 00 to FF hex. The eight-bit unit is so common in computers that it has its own name, the 'byte'. A byte of data can be defined as any value that can be expressed using a maximum of eight bits.

There are other terms relating to the binary numbering system that are worth noting. When the individual bits of a value are referred to, they are numbered in order of value. Therefore, bit 0 of a number is the last bit written down (the 'rightmost' bit) and holds the 'zero or one' data — that is, it indicates whether a number is odd or even. The phrase 'least significant bit' (LSB) is sometimes used for bit 0. In an eight-bit value, the 'most significant bit' (MSB) would be bit 7, the 'leftmost' bit.

Another term used to define a group of bits is 'nibble', which is four bits, or half a byte. The low nibble of a byte consists of bits 0 to 3, the high nibble bits 4 to 7.

Binary data can be handled in larger units than bytes. A 'word' is 16 bits, or two bytes, and a 'long word' is 32 bits, or four bytes. Just as the most significant nibble of a byte is the upper four bits, so the most significant word of a long word is the upper group of 16 bits.

We will come to use all the above terms when describing binary numbers: bits, nibbles and bytes are important to the concept of all computers, and we will meet words and long words when describing the QL itself.

How the computer uses binary data

I have already mentioned that the QL has an internal data structure of eight lines or columns which relay the separate bits around the computer — these lines are known collectively as the 'data bus'. The information that travels along this bus can only be accurately described as data because at different times the contents of the bus will have a different significance. On occasions, the data bus will hold a value that the computer is treating as a simple number; at other times the data may be representing a 'machine code instruction' — more of which in Chapter 4.

Representing characters

Another possibility is that the data present on the bus is representing a 'character'. Each character you type into the QL — whether it is a figure, a letter of the alphabet, punctuation, control code (such as ENTER) or whatever — has a unique eight-bit code. A character is therefore processed as a byte. Of these bytes, or 'character codes', those in the range 0 to 127 conform to a standard called ASCII (American Standard Code

23

for Information Interchange). For example, the letter A has the ASCII code 65 dec (41 hex). You can look up the other ASCII codes in the QL User Guide — they are fairly standard throughout the computer industry.

Note that standard ASCII only uses values that can be resolved as a seven-bit number, but the data bus can hold an eight-bit value. The wasted bit is used on the QL to allow additional character codes in the range 128 to 255, which provide graphic symbols and the like.

Representing large numbers

A data bus which can only hold numbers up to FF hex presents a problem when we want a computer to manipulate very large, or even very small, values. In order to pass a word of data (16 bits), the data bus is used twice, sending two bytes, in serial fashion, one after the other. This is how the QL's integer values are handled.

'Floating point' numbers are stored and transmitted in much the same manner, but to increase the range a possible six bytes are used, with one byte representing the scale of the number and the others giving the digits. For example, the value 1117 can be written as $1.117 * 10^3$ (10 to the power of 3). One byte of the floating point representation would hold the 10^3 scaling value (called the 'exponent'), while the other bytes would store the 1.117 (called the 'mantissa'). The QL's inbuilt software takes care of the translation of real values into the serial six-byte form.

The Address Bus

Inside the QL, and all other digital computers, there is a data bus for the transmission of values. In addition, a second bus is used to convey 'addresses'. Computers are equipped with memory devices with which to store data, and each of the memory locations needs to be identified with some form of label so that the computer can distinguish between them. The simplest analogy is that of a bank of pigeon holes, each of which can contain a number (0 to 255). In order for the computer to locate the correct pigeon hole, and therefore find the value stored in it, the pigeon holes each have a unique address — hole 2 may hold the byte 20, hole 3 the byte 40, and so on.

These addresses need to be passed to the memory circuits, and this is achieved by the 'address bus'. The size, or width, of this bus dictates how many memory locations the computer can address — an eight-bit address bus would only be able to address 256 memory locations. The QL is handsomely equipped with a 20-bit address bus, which means it is capable of hosting up to 1,048,576 individual memory locations. In Chapter 3 we will see how the address and data buses are used together when the computer fetches or stores information in its memory circuits.

It is worth a short digression at this point to explain a piece of computer jargon which can be confusing. Advertisements and computer literature frequently describe a computer as having a certain amount of memory, in the case of the QL, 128K bytes. As K is the SI unit for a thousand (ie the internationally accepted standard), it would be natural to assume that 128K bytes means 128,000 bytes. In computer terminology, however, 1K means the amount of memory that can be addressed by 10 bits, which works out at 1024 memory locations. This 'small' discrepancy makes 128K actually mean 130,712 (20000 hex).

Other numbering conventions

Before leaving the subject of numbers, there are two conventions associated with binary values which we should examine — two's complement and binary coded decimal. These will crop up when we discuss machine code.

Two's complement

The convention of 'two's complement' arithmetic allows negative numbers to be represented. For the system to work, we must stick with the same size of binary number for all calculations — the most significant bit is used to indicate the sign. In the case of byte-sized two's complement numbers, bit 7 is used to indicate whether a number is positive or negative, and numbers can be expressed in the range −128 to +127. If bit 7 is 0, the number is positive and the low seven bits give it a value in the range 0 to 127. If bit 7 is 1, however, the number is negative and can be calculated in the following manner. Invert each bit of the number (this process is known as complementing), then subtract 1. The number remaining, with a minus sign in front, is the value of the byte.

The usefulness of this convention can be seen when we add two numbers together. In the case of byte-sized numbers, as long as no notice is taken of any overflow into a theoretical bit 8 (as it would come from the 'sign' bit), adding a negative number to a positive one will result in the correct answer. A simple example is the addition of −1 (11111111 bin) to +1 (00000001). Add the two together and the eight-bit result is 00000000 bin — the 1 carried into the 'ninth' bit is lost and the answer is zero. Perhaps you might like to try a few numbers yourself, using the base conversion program and good old pencil and paper.

Binary coded decimal

Often shortened to BCD, this is a convention for storing numbers to the base 10. Each byte holds two digits, one in each nibble: the nibbles each hold a value in the range 0 to 9. Because the four bits of a nibble can actually represent the values 10 to 16 as well, these bit patterns are considered illegal, and therefore the way in which you manipulate BCD needs to take this into account. The QL's microprocessor has special machine code instructions for dealing in BCD. Although it is quite possible to avoid the use of it, BCD does have some advantages in certain applications, such as numerical displays.

CHAPTER 3
Microprocessor Systems

The Sinclair QL computer is a highly advanced product, and therefore it is also a complex one. For the benefit of newcomers to computer hardware, the next few chapters of this book will look at an idealised, and vastly simplified, microcomputer system, in order to help distinguish the wood from the trees. We are concerned here with the principles behind personal computers in general — the architecture and operation of the QL will be covered in Section 2.

Take a close look at **Figure 3.1**. It represents the main components required to implement a digital computer. At the heart of the system is a microprocessor — the Central Processing Unit (CPU). Although this is the most important component, it needs some vital support. There are two different types of memory device shown in the diagram — the Read Only Memory (ROM) which holds permanent data, and the Random Access Memory (RAM), which stores data on a temporary basis. Some of the RAM has a special purpose — it is called the Video RAM because it is used to hold information which the Video Display Chip translates into a picture to be viewed on a monitor or television set. The Keyboard Interface can take many forms: its purpose is to allow the CPU to fetch a byte of data from the keyboard. Finally, the diagram shows two components which are required to give 'life' to the microprocessor — the reset switch is a way of providing a 'start' signal, and the clock circuit gives a series of pulses that act as a pacemaker.

In the not too distant past all computers filled whole rooms and the component parts were housed in separate packages, according to their function. If you had been shown round such an installation, your attention may have been directed towards 'memory' in the grey boxes over there, or to the 'punched-tape reader' here. Your guide may have indicated one of the anonymous grey cabinets and said, 'That's where the actual work takes place; it's the Central Processing Unit.'

Computers have now shrunk in size, but if you look inside one you can still point to one integrated circuit and say, 'that's where the work is done'. These CPUs contain all the components which used to be found in that grey cabinet, etched on to a slice of silicon of tiny proportions. Other sections of the computer, although difficult to distinguish, can also be treated as if they were individual components.

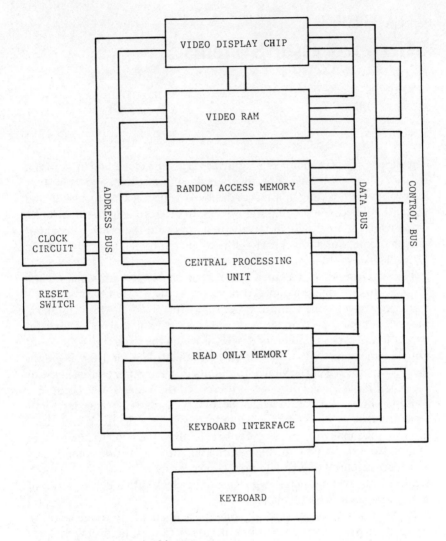

Figure 3.1: Computer Architecture

Before we look (at the end of the chapter) at how the parts of Figure 3.1 work together, let's examine the more important of them individually, beginning with the CPU.

The central processing unit
The first step in understanding the workings of a CPU involves us in looking at the inputs and outputs, rather than examining its contents. It

is at this point that I intend to start — we will look inside the box in the next chapter.

Most microprocessors have at least 40 terminal pins connecting them to the outside world. Whilst some of these are for inputting, and others for outputting, voltages, some of them can perform both functions.

Voltage connections

To deal with the simplest first, let us study the two pins which provide the integrated circuit (IC) with its power. For its internal operations, and also for outputting signals to other devices, the IC needs a source of voltage difference. A +5V supply applied to the Vcc pin relative to the 0V attached to the earth, or GND, pin, will serve this purpose. The amount of current that will flow through the CPU varies according to the function being performed, but it will never be very great.

Data pins

We have already met the concept of a data bus. One of these flows around the computer to allow data to be passed between the various components. The CPU communicates with the data bus through its 'data pins'. Most microprocessors, including the 68008 chip used by the QL, have eight such pins, and these are numbered D0 to D7. The pins are bi-directional. On some occasions, the eight pins are pulled high or low by the CPU in order to impose a byte of data on the data bus to be used elsewhere. At other times, the CPU reads in data, placed on the bus by other devices, through its data pins, and when this is happening these pins are floating.

Pins that are capable of assuming a floating state are very useful, and therefore very commonly found on computer integrated circuits. Chips built with such pins are known as 'tri-state' devices — they allow you to connect many things to the same data bus without the components interfering with each other, except when this is required.

Address pins

Now that we have a method of passing data in and out, we need to control where it is fetched from or sent to. For this purpose, microprocessors are equipped with 'address pins' which control the address bus. These allow the processors to signal which one of their surrounding devices they wish to communicate with. Modern microprocessors have at least 16 address pins, allowing 64K separate destinations. (The 68008 boasts 20 such pins, giving 1M — 1 megabyte — of addresses.)

Control pins

The third set of signals which flow around the computer are often grouped together under the title of 'control bus'. In order to understand the simple system illustrated in Figure 3.1, we need only interest ourselves in two such signals, READ (RD) and WRITE (WR). Whereas the address bus is used to indicate the address of the device which the CPU wants to communicate with, the RD and WR pins signal to the device in which direction the CPU wants the flow of information to go. If the WR pin is active, the CPU wishes to store data: if the RD pin is active, the CPU wants to retrieve information. To do this, some types of CPU will pull the pin low, while others will pull it high; a low active signal is indicated by placing a bar above the name. Regardless of the CPU design, when the CPU wishes to activate a signal on the control bus, we say that it 'asserts' the particular line.

Two further pins of the CPU (CLK and RESET) will be of interest when we come to look at the workings of our simplified system. Both of these are committed to other components shown in Figure 3.1, which we will now examine.

The clock circuit

The pin of the CPU which connects to the clock circuit is normally called CLK, short for clock. Through this pin, the processor needs to receive a series of pulses which will act as its heartbeat. In order to make the CPU function, its CLK pin must be pulled alternately high and low by an external voltage source: the clock circuit which performs this task, based on a type of electronic circuit called an 'oscillator', generates a varying voltage in a form known as a 'square wave'. The output of the clock circuit is high for a fixed period of time and then falls low for the same duration, performing this task continually. The cycle of a square wave is the same as for the sine waves looked at in Chapter 1, and we measure the speed of all alternating voltages in units named 'hertz'.

The operating speed of computer clock circuits is upwards of 1M Hz, considerably higher than the audible sound frequencies mentioned in Chapter 2. Each time the microprocessor senses that its clock input pin has received a new cycle of square wave from the clock circuit, it performs the next task. So the clock circuit acts as a time-keeper for the CPU, regulating its actions and prompting it to perform the next function.

With all the complex circuitry that a microprocessor contains, why can't it regulate its own speed, or, even simpler, run as fast as it can? The main reason for using an external clock circuit is that it gives circuit designers control over the CPU, and allows them to build a computer in which all the associated circuitry can keep pace with the main microprocessor. It also gives them the facility to stop the clock, as it were, to freeze all action until the clock circuit is turned on again.

The reset switch

The remaining pin of the CPU which requires our attention is the RESET pin; the circuitry attached to this amounts to little more than a switch. When this reset switch is operated (either manually, or automatically when the computer is switched on), it places zero volts on the reset pin. The effect on the CPU is as the pin's name implies — whether the CPU was working on a program, or had just been turned on and was therefore in a state of confusion, a RESET signal forces the processor to commence work from a predetermined point, regardless of its condition before the signal. This is, if you like, the 'go' signal.

Memory devices — ROM and RAM

The time has come to expand on the memory circuits used by computers. Memory is used by your QL to store the data it needs in order to function, whether that data is the machine code the QL uses when it is switched on, the programs from this book, or commercial software loaded from the microdrive. There are essentially two distinct types of memory used in microcomputers, and we have already touched on these.

Read only memory (ROM), does not allow the microprocessor to alter its data: as its name implies, it can only be 'read from'. Random access memory (RAM) is a slightly confusing title because its main feature is the facility to have its contents altered under the control of the computer. Of course, the situation is not as simple as this sounds: both RAM and ROM can be subdivided into further different types. The QL is equipped with the most common versions of both types of memory — mask-etched ROM and dynamic RAM.

ROM

Let us begin looking at read only memory devices by studying the type of ROM which your QL uses to store its operating system and language software. A typical mask-etched ROM is capable of storing 128K bits, organised as 16K bytes of data.

Input and output

A 128K bit ROM has 28 pins, although some of these do not serve any purpose other than to allow the chip to fit the same socket as other breeds of ROM. There are 14 address pins, which attach to the computer's

31

address bus so that the ROM can decode the address signals sent by the CPU. A further eight data pins are provided to allow the ROM to put signals on to the data bus, while a supply voltage of +5V must be provided through the ROM's Vcc and GND pins. Perhaps the most important pin is the 'chip select' (CS) terminal — when asserted, this activates the ROM and causes it to output data through its data pins.

Behaviour of a ROM

The example ROM which we are discussing holds 16K bytes of data which are 'built in' at the time of manufacture. Each of these bytes may be of any value in the 0 to 255 range, and each individual byte has its own unique address, in the range 0 to 16,384. When the CS pin is asserted, the ROM reacts by looking at the address which is present on its address pins. The byte of data stored inside the ROM which has that address is then placed on the data pins. If we only required a system with 16K of ROM addresses (and no RAM), we could connect the CS pin of the ROM directly to the 'read' signal from the CPU's control signal pins. If the CPU placed, for example, the address 100 hex on the address bus and asserted its read signal, the ROM would respond by placing the byte of data with the address 100 hex on to its data pins and back to the CPU via the data bus.

Address decoding

Computers need to be able to use the whole range of addresses available to them: in the above hypothetical case, the ROM takes no account of the state of bits 14 (ie the fifteenth bit) and above of the address bus, and it would therefore respond in the same manner if 4100 hex were given out as the address (bit 14 high) as it does for 100 hex. In order to avoid this problem, computers are equipped with address decoding logic that controls the CS pins of the memory devices so that they 'map in' to various addresses. For example, a computer with a 16-bit address bus could be designed with 16K of ROM memory which responded to addresses 4000 to 7FFF hex, and logic gates would monitor address bits 14 and 15 as well as the read signal. The logic of the circuit would be such that, when bit 14 was high, bit 15 low and read asserted, the CS pin of the ROM was also asserted. Any other combination would leave this additional ROM (at addresses 4000 to 7FFF hex) dormant; its data pins would remain floating so as not to affect the data bus. In this case, the memory decoding circuits would activate whichever ROM or RAM chips were designated to be at the given address.

Inside the mask-etched ROM

Each single bit of data held by a mask-etched ROM is in the form of a simple connection. Imagine that each memory cell is nothing more than a length of wire, with one end connected to address decoding logic circuits present inside the chip, and the other end attached to one of the data pins. If the wire is continuous, a signal sent by the address decoding logic will be transmitted to a data pin; if it is cut then no signal will be passed on. The data pins themselves have buffer circuits attached: the pins will be kept floating until CS is asserted. When enabled they will be pulled low unless a high signal is passed to them through one of the memory cells.

Each byte of data stored has eight single-bit memory cells, each of which is attached to a different data pin. The group of eight cells are all attached to one addressing signal, which is only asserted if that particular byte's address has been sent to the internal memory decoding logic.

From the above description, you can see that an awful lot of connections need to be made, or not made, depending on the data the ROM is to hold. If every single bit stored were to be a logic 1 then 128K connections are required. The manufacturers use a photographic process to etch the connections on to the silicon material of the chip itself. The 'template', or 'mask', used in this process is very expensive, but once made, the cost of producing each chip is low, so these mask-etched ROMs are only economical for large production runs.

PROMs and EPROMs

It is worth mentioning two other types of ROM that you may encounter. The 'programmable read only memory' (PROM) is a device which comes off the production line containing no useful information, but can then have data stored in it by a programming machine. This is a 'once only' process — the individual memory cells are all set to 1, that is, all the connections are made, before the programming begins. The data is altered by a machine generating high voltages which 'blow' the individual memory cell connections in much the same way as a fuse behaves if too great a voltage is applied to it.

An improved version, the 'erasable programmable read only memory' (EPROM), stores data as electrical charges. Not only can it be programmed, but also, if necessary, the data can be erased by the application of ultra-violet light through a small window on its upper surface.

Both of the above memory devices are used mainly for small production runs and prototypes, and they are often 'pin compatible' with normal ROMs. This simply means that they will fit the same sockets and have their pins in the same places. The early prototype QL computers were fitted with EPROMs, so that they could be fully tested before the programs were committed to the expensive tooling-up procedure required to make ROMs for production machines.

The most important aspect to notice about all ROMs is that they will retain their contents at all times, whether they are powered up or not, because, although they need a voltage supply to operate the decoding circuits they contain, the data is stored in a 'non-volatile' form. This is an essential facility for any computer that is to be turned on and off, so that when it is first switched on there are always some instructions ready and waiting.

RAM

Memory which can contain only data that has been preprogrammed is of no use when we want to use memory to store data that the computer can change, so computers are supplied with random access memory, with which they can write data to locations for later retrieval. The name refers to the fact that locations can be accessed for either reading or writing in any order. Note that the term random access could be applied to the programmable types of ROM I have mentioned, but it has come to be used only for the forms of memory that can be written to.

The simplest type of RAM can be thought of as a ROM layout with address lines and decoding circuits but, instead of the links, each line of information has a flip-flop arrangement of which the output represents each 'bit' of data. This output is routed to the appropriate data line when the correct address is fed on to the address bus. Also the data pins are bidirectional, so with the aid of pins to tell the chip whether to output or input information, the CPU can send data along with an address to the memory, and it will set the values of the appropriate flip-flops to those of the data sent. This kind of memory is called 'static RAM', because as long as it is receiving a supply voltage it will maintain the pattern of bits which its internal circuitry is storing.

However, this type of memory is expensive and is difficult to make compact, so it will come as no surprise to you to learn that the QL, in common with most computers, is equipped with a different breed, called 'dynamic RAM'. This stores data in the form of an electrical charge in the gate area of a transistor. This voltage, unfortunately, begins to leak away after a short period of time, so the memory needs the opportunity to refresh the charges before they are lost, by reading out the values and restoring them at suitable intervals. The signals and circuitry required for this 'refreshing' operation are complex — some processors have special facilities to help. Nevertheless, the advantages of dynamic memory chips still outweigh the disadvantages, and from a user's point of view there is no difference between the performances of static or dynamic RAMs.

Keyboard and video circuits

Before we see how our simplified system works, I will briefly mention the keyboard and video circuits. These take many forms. The video-generating section needs to have access to the area of memory that has been designated for screen display. The possible clashes that might ensue between it and the CPU when they both want to use the same memory, are solved in a variety of ways, and we will look at these in Chapter 10. In addition, the different ways of coding the screen data vary, and these will also be covered in Chapter 10.

As for the keyboard, this can be thought of as a particular memory address which, when read by the CPU, puts a byte corresponding to the ASCII code of the key currently being pressed on to the data bus.

How the components work together

Let's now 'power up' the model computer in Figure 3.1 and follow what happens. All the circuits begin to receive the voltage they require in order to function. The oscillator circuit starts to apply the square wave clock signal to the CPU. To bring the computer into life at this point, we must operate the reset switch.

The first thing that happens is that the value 0 is placed on the address bus — that is, all the address pins of the CPU will be set to 0 volts. The RD pin will be asserted. The microprocessor has now generated sufficient information to tell its associated circuitry that it requires the data stored in memory location 0 to be placed on the data bus. The ROM recognises the address as one of its own, responds and goes about the task of retrieving the data and placing it on the bus. The CPU waits for the next clock pulse: it then assumes that the data on the data bus is that provided by the memory, and so reads this data through its data pins. What the CPU has fetched is its first instruction and, still using clock pulses as a timing reference, it will go about the business of carrying out that instruction.

To follow the system in action, we now need to delve inside the processor, which brings us to the next chapter.

CHAPTER 4
The Processor at Work

The contents of the CPU

In our study of a simple microcomputer, we have, so far, treated the CPU as a single component. To understand the manner in which a CPU works, and to be able to comprehend how it is possible to program it to carry out useful tasks, it is now necessary to look at the contents of the integrated circuit.

The processor at the heart of the QL, the Motorola 68008, is a highly advanced chip. In the same way in which I have introduced you to a simplified model of a computer, we will now study a theoretical CPU chip. The example will contain all the important parts of a microprocessor, and later in the chapter we will actually follow its actions as it 'runs' a program. When we meet the 68008 CPU, in Section 2 of this book, you will see that, although it is a more complex design than our model, the principles involved are the same.

Take a look at **Figure 4.1**. It represents the contents of our model microprocessor. There are three fundamentally separate areas, connected by a network of internal buses — a number of 'registers', which are no more than local memory cells, the Arithmetic and Logic Unit (ALU), and the Control Unit, which is the section which performs the instructions.

Internal buses

The internal data bus shown in the diagram allows data to be transferred between registers and the ALU. Both internal buses (data and address) can also communicate with the external buses of the computer via the pins of the CPU. They are not in direct contact, however — 'buffer' circuits, under the direction of the control unit, allow the buses to interact only at the right moments, transferring information between the CPU and the external buses when required. At times the internal buses, and particularly the data bus, are used totally independently of the external lines.

Registers

The registers, six of which are shown in Figure 4.1, are fast-acting eight or

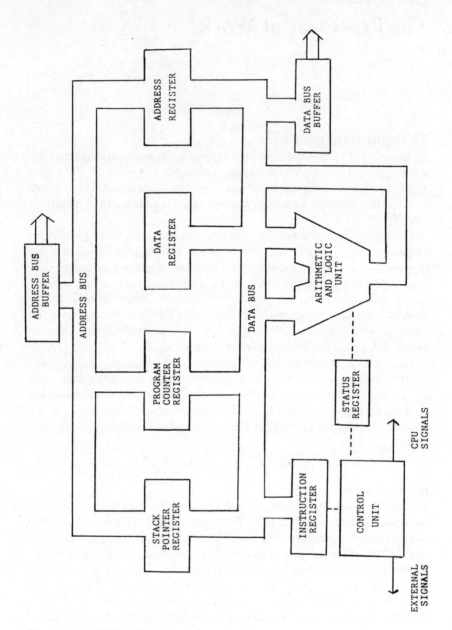

Figure 4.1: A Model Microprocessor

16-bit memory circuits under the direct command of the control unit. Information is passed between them, the ALU and the outside world along the internal data bus. Some of the registers are also capable of sending information out on the address bus.

All processors need a program counter register, often called the PC; and normally present is at least one stack pointer register, or SP. The two registers marked as Data and Address registers are the main working registers and, although our model has only one of each type, CPUs often boast many more. It is worth noting that some microprocessors make no distinction between data and address types, having general-purpose 'Jack of all trades' registers, but our model makes the distinction because the 68008 has a set of registers devoted to each role.

The Status register is, in effect, eight single-bit memory locations: these are used by the control unit and ALU to record certain events. Sometimes the single bits are referred to as 'flags'. The information held in the status register can be used by the programmer or by the control unit itself.

The Instruction register is used to store the last machine code instruction read in: it is not available to the programmer and can almost be considered as a part of the control unit.

Arithmetic and logic unit

The ALU is responsible for the processing of data — it can be thought of as the CPU's own internal calculator. The capabilities of this will vary between types of processor: all ALUs will certainly be capable of adding two binary values together and returning the result to the data bus; they will also subtract and perform logic operations such as AND. Operations such as multiply and divide are beyond the scope of most ALUs — the 68008 is capable of these, but its ALU needs help from the control unit and the process takes some time.

The control unit

This is really the nerve centre of any CPU: control unit signals reach all other sections of the chip — they manage the buffers, registers and ALU. The movement of information, both internal and via the external lines, as well as the interpreting of instructions into the required action, are the control unit's responsibility.

What happens inside the CPU

Let us now build up a picture of what goes on inside the CPU. Many of the events which occur are similar in principle, if not in detail. The series of operations which follow the receipt of a reset signal are also the first few steps which a CPU will take in following a machine code program. If you refer back to Chapter 3, you will recall that our simple model of a CPU always responds to a reset signal by fetching the data from memory location 0 and then treating this as its first instruction. The value, and therefore meaning, of this instruction makes no difference to the actual fetching process. We shall begin our study of the internal operations of a CPU with the sensing of a reset signal.

Fetching data from memory

When the control unit senses the reset, its first response is to order the program counter register to clear all its bits to 0. The CPU now waits for a clock pulse: when this arrives the next event is triggered. The contents of the PC (which are now 0) are placed on the internal address bus, and the address bus buffers ordered to extend this signal through the address pins to the computer's address bus. The control unit then asserts the RD signal, and the CPU waits for external memory to respond. As we saw, the memory circuits which relate to the address 0, which we have deemed to be ROM locations, respond by placing their contents on to the data bus.

Having waited a clock cycle to give the memory circuits time to act, the control unit then enables the buffers on the data bus to transmit the byte of data to the internal data bus. The control unit also sends a signal to the instruction register, telling it to memorise whatever is now present on the data bus.

So, after two clock cycles, the contents of memory address 0 have been transferred to the instruction register — not exactly an earth-shattering achievement, but, on a system with a clock speed of 1 megahertz (which is quite slow by the QL's standards), this would only take 0.00002 seconds!

Incrementing the program counter

Before acting on the instruction data which it has just fetched, the CPU carries out a different task with the aid of the ALU. The requirement is to increment the PC, that is, add 1 to its contents — the reason for doing this will be explained in a moment. How the hardware of the CPU does this is of interest, though, as it is typical of many other operations that the CPU will need to perform.

The PC needs to store the same number of bits as the processor has address pins; any less and it would not be able to generate all the possible addresses at which there may be memory circuits. If we assume that our model processor has 16 address pins, then it will have a 16-bit PC. Many ALUs, however, are not capable of handling as many as 16 bits at one time. Let us assume that our ALU is eight bits wide, that is to say it can add two bytes of data together, resulting in up to a nine-bit number (255 + 255 = 510, 111111110 bin). The problem which the CPU must solve is, 'how do I add a value to a 16-bit number if I can only add together eight-bit numbers?'

The first step of the addition is to add 1 to the low byte of the PC. To do this the control unit causes the PC to transmit its low eight bits to the internal data bus, and it also signals to the ALU to store the resulting state of the bus (ie the value of the low byte) in one half of its circuits. An 'add 1' signal is then sent to the ALU, so it sets the other half of its circuitry to represent 00000001.

The contents of these two halves are added together by an electronic process, one bit at a time, as follows. A logic circuit examines the least significant bits of both values which the ALU holds (the LSB is bit 0, see Chapter 2). If both are 0, a logic 0 is transmitted back to the LSB of the data bus. If either, but not both, is 1, a logic 1 is sent to the bit 0 line of the data bus. If they are both 1, an overflow in the binary arithmetic has occurred, and the ALU places 0 on the data bus, but passes a 1 to the circuits which deal with the next significant bit (bit 1) of the addition.

The ALU has now added the first column of the binary sum together, passed the result back to the relevant bit of the internal data bus, and passed any carry that occurred on to the next column. Circuits for the second and subsequent bits of the eight-bit addition act in a similar manner, but also take into account the carry bit that may have been passed on. If all three bits of the column (one from each value and the overflow from the previous column) happen to be 1, a logic 1 is passed back to the data bus as well as a carry to the next column.

The eighth and final column (bit 7 of the addition) has no 'next column' for its carry, but this carry is an important value: it tells us if the whole of the addition resulted in an overflow. This is precisely the kind of information that the status register is designed to hold — the carry from the addition is placed in the 'carry flag' bit of the status register for future use.

Take a moment to think over what has just been performed. The CPU has added two numbers together using logic circuits: this is not particularly magical, as the circuits simply followed the logic rules to which they adhere. The result of the addition is now present on the CPU's internal data bus — all the control unit needs to do now is signal to the lower half of the PC register to store what is on the data bus.

The least significant byte of the 16-bit PC has had 1 added to it; as it was previously 0, it now holds 1 (00000001 bin). What would have happened if it had started out as 11111111 bin (255 dec)? Adding 00000001 bin would result in an overflow in each column, with 00000000 bin appearing as the result on the data bus, and a note of an overflow in the carry flag of the status register. Remember that we have only processed the low byte of the PC; there is also the upper half to take into account with regard to the possibility of a carry. The high byte of the PC is fetched into one half of the ALU, and the value of the carry flag placed in the lowest column of the other half of the ALU's circuits — the other bits are cleared. A second addition is now performed and the result stored in the upper byte of the PC.

How the CPU obeys programs

We have now seen how the hardware of the CPU works when performing operations such as fetching data from memory, passing it around its internal data bus between registers and the ALU, and processing that data using arithmetic and logical rules. The next stage in understanding the CPU involves us in examining the way in which it can obey programs supplied by us, the users.

Machine code

Computer languages vary greatly in complexity. At the top of the scale, 'high level' languages are close to human language. In SuperBASIC, the QL's standard language, instructions such as 'IF Total = 0 THEN PRINT "The total is zero" ' are simple enough for us to understand, but the SuperBASIC interpreter has a great deal of translation work to do before the CPU can carry out the task we have set. At the other end of the scale the lowest level language that exists is the 'machine code' in which the microprocessor deals. Any high level instruction must be translated into code before it is executed; by programming a computer in machine code we make things harder for ourselves, but much quicker for the CPU.

When a dog has been well trained, it will respond to the command 'sit'. It recognises the sound made, and so responds, but it is possible to train a dog to sit by using *any* word. A microprocessor responds to a machine code instruction because it has been designed to do so — different processors have different machine languages, even though they can perform similar tasks. These tasks, carried out in response to instructions, are not complex — fetching information from memory and external devices; performing simple arithmetic and processing the information; sending information to be stored in memory or to activate external devices. These simple functions can be built up into complex processes that appear almost intelligent in operation, but this depends on the skill of the programmer in manipulating the instructions available.

We have studied a simplified CPU at the centre of a model microcomputer. I will now introduce a few hypothetical machine code instructions which our CPU responds to: remember that they are nothing more than arbitrary codes which I have deemed to be instructions to which our simple processor responds. We will meet 'real' machine code in Chapter 7.

Table 4.1 lists the instruction set of our simple model — each instruction has a code and a 'mnemonic'. When the data shown in the code column is in the CPU's instruction register and translated into action, the operation carried out is unique to that code, and it is loosely described by the mnemonic. A study of the table will show you that the instruction which has the code 1 has the mnemonic CLR D: this is a shorthand representation of 'clear the contents of the data register to zero'. You could quickly memorise the six codes that are shown in Table 4.1, but true CPUs have many hundreds of codes, making them impossible to learn, so the mnemonics act as a convenient half-way stage between a full description and the actual codes.

Table 4.1: Model Instruction Set

Code	Instruction (mnemonic)	Description
1	CLR D	Set the Data register to zero
2	LD A,nn	Place the next two bytes in the Address register.
3	ADD D,n	Add the next byte to the Data register
4	LD (A),D	Load the memory location whose address is held in the Address register with the contents of the Data register.
5	HALT	Stop processing.

Running a program

We are now going to follow a machine code program in action, and see the CPU going about the tasks it is set. For the sake of this description, let us assume that our model computer has a ROM memory area that is located at addresses 0 to 1000h. A program is permanently stored in the memory locations but, in our example, this only occupies the first eight addresses, numbered 0 to 7.

You can see a listing of the program in **Table 4.2**. Don't muddle the tables together — Table 4.1 shows the types and values of instructions available, but Table 4.2 is the actual program which we will now follow through a step at a time. One further assumption that we will make about

Table 4.2: Model Program

Address	Contents	Instruction
0	1	CLR D
1	2	LD A,8000h
2	80	–
3	0	–
4	3	ADD D,40h
5	40	–
6	4	LD (A),D
7	5	HALT

our model computer is that all addresses, other than those of the ROM, access a RAM memory location.

Starting the program

You have seen what happens when the CPU receives a reset signal — this is the first step in the program we are now to run.

One clock cycle passes while the CPU loads its PC with 0, fetches the data from that address (0) and places it in the instruction register. The CPU then increments the value in the PC. The control unit now goes about the business of translating this first instruction, from address 0: you can see from Table 4.2 that this is code 1 — CLR D. Signals are sent to the data register, telling it to set all its bits to 0. When it responds, the first instruction has been obeyed — the data register now holds the value 0, whatever its previous contents.

The first instruction obeyed, it is time to fetch the next. The reason for incrementing the PC after fetching an instruction now becomes plain — if this were not done, then the next instruction would be collected from the same address as the previous one and the CPU would spend all its time executing the same instruction. Because of the increment, the PC is now pointing to ROM address 1 — on receipt of the next clock pulse, the contents of this location are transferred to the instruction register for translation, and the PC incremented again.

Here we are seeing the essence of 'sequential programming' — the steps of a program follow each other as sequential machine code instructions stored in adjacent memory locations. The CPU, whenever it fetches an instruction from a program, always follows the steps described earlier in this chapter so that the PC points to the next instruction to be executed.

Table 4.2 shows us that the code fetched as the second instruction is 2, mnemonic LD A,nn. By this I mean, 'load the address register with the next two bytes of data in the program memory area'. Although ROM addresses 2 and 3 are part of the program, they do not contain instructions: they form the 'immediate data' for the instruction at address 1. To obey the command, the CPU carries out a memory fetch cycle using the PC and incrementing it as if it were fetching an instruction. Instead of the number it collects being passed along the data buses to the instruction register, the first byte is stored in the upper byte of the address register, the second byte in the lower half. Each fetch and increment operation takes two clock cycles to perform, so obeying the LD A,nn instruction takes six cycles.

Let's take stock of the position. Eight cycles after the reset signal was received, the data register has been cleared, the contents of memory locations 2 and 3 (which from the table you can see are 80h and 00h) have been transferred to the address register, and the PC now points to ROM location 4.

So far, the program has just been causing the CPU to move data around, or clear registers. The next instruction, taken from address 4, has the value 3, mnemonic ADD D,nn, and actually uses the ALU to process data. ADD D,n means 'add to the data register the next value stored in program memory' — the data we wish to add is stored in the program as immediate data in the same manner as with the LD A,n. The PC is already pointing to the next byte (address 5, contents 40h), a fetch (and PC increment) is performed, and the value 40h sent to one half of the ALU. The contents of the data register are passed along the internal data bus to the other half of the ALU, and then the control unit orders that the two values are added together. This process is similar to that which we studied when the low byte of the PC had 1 added to it, with the result of the addition being passed back to the data register, which assumes this new value.

The add operation may have taken longer than the time available between the fetch and the next clock pulse, so one whole extra cycle is allowed for this event. ADD D,n takes five cycles to complete — two to fetch the instruction, two to fetch the immediate data, and one to perform the addition. To date, our sample program has been running for 13 clock cycles. The address register holds the value 8000h, the data register 40h (00 + 40h being the last operation), and the PC is pointing to ROM address 6.

The next instruction fetched, LD (A),D, code 4, causes the memory location of which the address is held in the address register to be loaded with the data stored in the data register. The brackets around the 'A' show that it is not the register itself which is loaded with the contents of D. When the control unit recognises this instruction, it orders the address register to place its contents on the internal address bus. The address bus buffer circuits are enabled, and the address is passed out to the external memory circuitry: the data register's contents are likewise sent to the computer's data bus. The control unit waits a clock pulse to be sure that the signals have reached the computer buses, and then it asserts the WR signal. Another clock cycle passes while the memory circuits are given time to store the data at the correct RAM location (8000h), and then the CPU moves on to its next instruction.

The final instruction fetched, from location 7, is code 5, mnemonic HALT, and it causes the control unit to cease operations. It simply means 'stop work'.

What have we achieved with our example program? In a remarkably short space of time (18 clock cycles) we have added two numbers together and placed the result in a particular location in memory. Machine code never does much more than this — it may need a great many instructions to do anything worthwhile, but then, at the speed at which that micro-processors work, this is not a problem.

Common machine code operations

If you have followed all that has been said so far in this chapter, then you should have a picture of what happens inside a microprocessor when it is running a machine code program. Remember that all programs, even those written in BASIC or other high level languages, end up as machine code when executed by the CPU.

In the simple examples used in the above routine and listed in Table 4.1, we have seen four types of operation: clearing a register, moving data around, addition, and halting the program. The rest of this chapter will explain further these types of operation and also explore the other classes of instruction. As these are all examples, I will give the names in full for clarity, whereas individual machine codes will use shortened names (mnemonics) which will differ from one type of CPU to another.

Moving data — addressing modes

This is the most common type of operation performed in programs: the power of a processor depends largely on the versatility of its moving instructions. The basic form comprises the instruction 'move the data held at the source to the destination' — the more choices of how source and destination are defined, the more powerful the processor.

To define the possibilities, we talk of the 'addressing modes' available, that is, the ways in which we can access data. A phrase which we will encounter often is 'effective address' (EA). If the EA is the 'source', it is the place where the data we are moving is actually held; if it is the 'desti-nation', it is where the data will end up. Let us look at some different addressing modes.

Immediate addressing is used by the instruction LOAD A,nn to specify the source of data. Immediate data is contained within the program itself, and occupies the memory space immediately following the instruction.

EA = next bits, bytes or words of instruction.

Register direct (also known as **direct**) addressing is used if data is transferred to or from another register. An instruction that loads data into a register is using direct addressing to specify the effective address of the destination.

EA = CPU register.

Indirect addressing is shown in our example code, LOAD (A),D. Here, the effective address is not the register itself, but that memory location of which the address is held by the A register. In our example program, the A register held the value 8000h, so the destination was the memory location 8000h.

EA = value held in CPU register.

Absolute addressing supplies the address from within the program. The information is stored in the same manner as immediate data, but is used as the effective address. Brackets are used to indicate absolute, as well as indirect, addressing — LOAD D, (8000h) would load the data register with the value held in memory location 8000h.

EA = location pointed to by next bytes of program.

Implied addressing means that the effective address is either non-existent or implicit in the instruction. In our example, CLEAR D, the source is 0. Implied addressing can be used to describe jump codes, for example, which, as we will see, imply that the PC is the destination.

EA is predetermined by instruction.

Program counter relative addressing can be seen as an extension of immediate addressing. If a CPU can specify a source or destination defined by the current value of the PC, plus or minus a displacement (supplied as immediate data) or an index value (taken from a register), then it is said to be capable of PC relative addressing. This is useful for writing 'relocatable' code which, by avoiding absolute addressing, can reside anywhere in memory.

EA = value in PC +/− displacement and/or index.

Should the above list not be daunting enough, there are many possible subdivisions and extensions. We will meet others when we examine the 68008 in detail, but for now remember that the above definitions are the basic types of addressing used. I will now present examples of moving instructions, and before you read on, work out for yourself the addressing modes employed.

LOAD (A),n: Place the next byte of the program in the memory location whose address is held in the A register.

LOAD (nn),D: Store the contents of the D register at the address given by the next bytes of program.

CLEAR A: Load the A register with 0.

Now for the answers! The destination of LOAD (A),n is pointed to by A, so the mode used is *indirect*, and the source is *immediate* data. LOAD (nn),D uses the *absolute* mode for its destination, and the source is *direct* from a register. In the third example, CLEAR A, the destination is again *direct*, but what is the effective address of the source, 0? It does not come from any particular place, but is *implied* by the instruction.

This last example is perhaps a bit sneaky, but if you had trouble with the first two I suggest you go over the definitions again. A clear understanding of effective address modes is important, particularly for the 68008 CPU.

Arithmetic and logic

The example of addition given earlier, ADD D,40h, added the immediate data 40h to the value held in the D register and then placed the result back in the D register. We are again looking at the idea of source and destination.

On simple processors it is only possible to have one destination, a register which is called the 'accumulator'. If you wish to add two values together, one of them must be placed in the accumulator, although the other number may come from a variety of effective addresses. The result of the addition will be left in the accumulator, destroying any record of its previous contents.

When CPUs allow more destinations, perhaps other registers or memory locations, the same rules apply — the previous contents of the destination are lost forever. Even a CPU as powerful as the 68008 does not have an instruction that will add the contents of two registers and place the answer in a third. Subtraction is normally possible, obeying the same format as addition, and some processors can multiply and divide. To allow for higher precision arithmetic, there are some instructions that include the carry bit (often called the 'extend' bit, or X bit) in a calculation. For example, if we wished to add two 16-bit numbers together, using an eight-bit CPU, the operation is treated as two eight-bit additions. The low order bytes of the numbers are added, and if a carry occurred from bit 7 into bit 8, the CPU would note this by setting the carry flag. In the second half of the addition, the instruction ADD WITH CARRY would not only add the high order bytes together, but also, if the carry was set, add a 1 to the result.

Apart from arithmetic, operations that affect the individual bits of values are also possible. Setting and resetting involves forcing a particular bit of a register or memory location to become 1 or 0.

Logic operations, such as AND and OR, allow two values to be treated, one bit at a time, in accordance with a particular logic law. Recalling the AND gate of Chapter 1, consider what happens if the values 00001111 bin and 01010101 bin are ANDed together. Bit 0 of the result will be 1, bit 1 will be 0, and so on, with the final result being 00000101 bin. These logic operations are very useful, particularly when dealing with external circuits (input/output, or I/O, operations), and in writing graphic routines.

A further form of binary manipulation is the idea of 'rotating' values. This is often done in conjunction with the carry bit; for example, if an eight-bit register is rotated right, the value of bit 0 goes into the carry bit, the value of bit 1 goes into bit 0, and so on until bit 7, which assumes the value of the carry. At first sight this may not appear very useful, but consider what has happened to the original value (assuming that the carry was not set) — by shifting all the bits one place to the right we have divided the value by two, and we even have a note in the carry bit if there was a remainder!

One final operation worth mentioning is 'compare'. This subtracts one value from another, discarding the answer. The two original values remain unchanged, but the status flags are set accordingly: if the numbers were the same, then the zero bit is set; if the numbers were different, the zero bit is cleared. We will see in a moment how this information can be used.

Jumping about
Having said that a CPU obeys instructions in a linear manner — obeying the code at location 0, then location 1 and so on — I must now introduce a class of commands that can alter the order of execution.

Consider the instruction JUMP to 2000h. If the CPU encounters this at any address, it reacts by loading the program counter with the value 2000h. The next instruction fetched is therefore taken from location 2000h: we have forced the processor to skip forward and ignore a large chunk of instructions. (We will find out how to return to the missed instructions in a moment.)

It is also possible to use a 'branch' instruction — this is a form of PC relative instruction, because it tells the CPU to jump forwards (or backwards) a number of locations. The specified amount is then added to (or subtracted from), the contents of the PC. These commands are useful because they allow the non-linear execution of code.

The most important feature is that the branching instructions can be 'conditional'. A good example is: BRANCH forward 10 addresses IF the zero bit is set. The CPU will react to this command by checking the zero bit of the status register: if this is set then the CPU will add 10 to the value of the PC. So we have a method of making decisions, based on the contents of the status register, and therefore on the result of the last operation which affected the flags. We can therefore divert the flow of the program if the result of a compare instruction, for example, proved two numbers to be the same. The conditional branching instructions are the means by which machine code programs perform 'IF x is true THEN do this' operations.

Stacking data

A 'stack' is an area of external memory used by the microprocessor to store data and addresses. Why, you may well ask, is a stack needed, and why does a special area have to be assigned? Let me outline the two basic uses made of the stack.

First, the CPU stores 'RETURN addresses' here. If you have written BASIC programs, you will already be familiar with subroutines. An often-used section of the program can be written just once: to execute it, we simply GOSUB whatever line number the routine starts at, and when the SuperBASIC interpreter reaches the end it encounters a RETURN instruction that tells it to go back to the part of the program immediately after the GOSUB which instigated the process.

The idea of subroutines is also very useful in machine code programming, particularly for performing those often-required simple tasks which use a lot of code. For example, printing a character to the screen may, on some systems, require a couple of hundred bytes of machine code. It would be nonsense to include these at every point in the program where the printing of a character is required, so the routine should be stored as a subroutine. After we have jumped to this routine, how do we get back to the point where we left off? Rather than jumping in the first place, we use the instruction 'JUMP to subroutine'. The CPU obeys this in the following manner.

Having fetched the instruction and incremented the PC as usual, the CPU stores the contents of the PC at the memory address pointed to by the stack pointer register (SP). The SP is then decremented so that it points below the stored address; the PC is loaded with the address of the subroutine and control is therefore passed over. When the subroutine is finished, returning to the calling program is achieved with a RETURN code. This increments the SP again, and loads the PC with the contents of memory pointed to by the SP. The CPU now goes back to the calling program: the SP contains its original value, but the code of the subroutine has been run. You can also call a subroutine from within another subroutine, as the SP is decremented each time to point to a fresh storage address.

The second use of the stack is the temporary storage of values. If you have a piece of data which you wish to retain but you have run out of registers, you can place it in external memory. To save you having to find free space, you can utilise the stack area by PUSHing the contents of the registers on to the stack. When you are ready to retrieve the data, you PULL it back from the stack into the desired register. This method is often used in conjunction with subroutines, as they may alter the contents of registers which are important to the calling routine: the data is placed on the stack and then salvaged before the RETURN instruction. Note that a disaster may occur if you push a value but forget to pull it before the return — instead of fetching an address, the CPU will fill the PC with the value and start executing code from totally the wrong place.

So the SP provides us with an almost automatic means of storage and retrieval of data from external memory, and allows the easy use of subroutines. To set up a stack we need only point the stack pointer at an area of RAM that will not be overwritten by the program, and ensure that there is sufficient space below this area for our purposes.

A stack is a LIFO data storage method, meaning Last In, First Out, and it is worth repeating here an often-used analogy. Imagine placing playing cards in a pile, or stack, on the table. You can only place cards on the top of the pile, and only retrieve the cards by picking up the top card first. Therefore, if you put down the ace of spades and then three more cards, you must remove those three before you can rescue the ace.

Since we examined our example program in Table 4.2, I have introduced additional classes of instruction. The time has come for an example that shows how these simple commands can be built up into a routine that actually does something.

The subroutine in **Table 4.3** is in the form of an assembler listing, but it does not bother with the opcodes or actual addresses. The first column contains labels, convenient names used to represent addresses within the program. The second column contains the instructions, and the last contains comments on what is happening. The program plays a tune, the notes of which are contained in a data table at the end of the routine. It is assumed that a sound-generating circuit is attached to the buses of the computer, and has two memory addresses allocated to it.

Address SOUNDFRQ sets the frequency of the note, so writing a value to this address will set the pitch. Address SOUNDDUR, when written to, commences the generation of the note, which lasts for a length of time

Table 4.3: Tune Routine

Tune Routine

Label	Instruction	Comments
TUNE	LOAD A, DATA	Load A with the address of the start of the tune data
LOOP	LOAD D, (A)	Load D with the value pointed to by the A register
	ADD D, 1	Point A to the next data item in the table
	COMPARE D, 0	If D is equal to zero, then set the zero flag
	BRANCH IF NOT EQUAL to PLAY	If the zero flag is not set, then jump to PLAY
	RETURN	End of program; return to calling routine
PLAY	LOAD SOUNDFRQ, D	Write pitch to sound circuits
	LOAD D, 8	Put duration into D register
	LOAD SOUNDDUR, D	Start note for duration of 8
	JUMP TO SUBROUTINE at DELAY	Go to the delay subroutine
	BRANCH to LOOP	Having returned here, branch to LOOP
DELAY	PUSH D	Store D on the stack
	LOAD D,80h	Set D to delay period
WAIT	SUBTRACT 1 FROM D	Reduce D by one and, if zero, set the zero flag
	BRANCH IF NOT EQUAL to WAIT	If the zero flag is not set, branch back to wait
	PULL D	Retrieve the original value of D from the stack
	RETURN	Return to calling routine
DATA	40h	Table of data for the tune
	46h	
	–	
	–	
	0	Zero indicates the end of the table

relative to the value written. So, by writing 20 to SOUNDFRQ, followed by 8 to SOUNDDUR, a note of pitch 20, duration 8, will emerge from the sound circuits of the computer.

If the program encounters a note of pitch 0, it assumes that the end of the tune has been reached, therefore we mark the end of the data table by placing a 0 there. Note also that a subroutine is used to generate a short delay between each note. This is not strictly necessary, but it is common practice as it allows other routines that may be added to use the delay routine. To help in this further, the D register is saved and restored, so the routine does not corrupt any registers. Enough said, I think, to help you follow the program. As you trace it through, try to picture the steps taken by the CPU.

SECTION 2
The Sinclair QL

CHAPTER 5
Introducing the QL

In the first section of this book, I described the general concepts of micro-computers from first principles. Now it is time to examine the workings of the Sinclair QL microcomputer specifically.

The QL is, on initial appraisal, a major break with the tradition of Sinclair Research computers. It uses a different processor and a radically new dialect of BASIC, comes complete with a fast tape storage system, and costs far more than any of its predecessors. On closer examination, however, there are similarities.

Previous products achieved their popularity by offering value for money and meeting a market need. The ZX80 was the first complete computer available for under £100 — it was unable to produce a TV display and compute at the same time; it possessed 4K of ROM, containing the operating system and a simple form of BASIC; and it included just 1K of RAM, paltry by today's standards and rather modest even in 1980. It was a success even with these limitations because it sold to people who wanted an off-the-shelf (or rather 'through-the-letterbox') computer aimed at novices and priced accordingly.

The ZX80 was soon replaced by the much improved, million-selling ZX81, with 8K of ROM and a 'slow' mode which maintained the screen display at the expense of very slow operation. These enhancements were combined with a price cut of £20 — soon Sinclair's silent, black and white, membrane-keyboarded computer was selling like hot cakes and opening up new markets, not only for computers but also for software, books and magazines.

May 1982 saw the launch of the ZX Spectrum. This represented a vast improvement on its predecessor, and in terms of value for money it was well ahead of the competition. A 16K model was only £5 dearer than a ZX81 with RAM pack, but the Spectrum offered a high resolution, eight-colour display, simple sound-making facilities and, at last, a moving keyboard. Also announced at the same time was the microdrive fast tape cartridge; although slow in arriving, the end product dramatically cut the cost of mass storage, compared with disks.

In January 1984, the QL was announced and caused much interest, not the least of which concerned delivery times. At the very end of April the first few machines reached their owners, with no SuperBASIC manual and the ROM port occupied with a 'kludge' containing the part of the operating system that would not fit into the originally-planned 32K of ROM.

Despite these setbacks, there was no shortage of orders for the QL. The machine is aimed directly at people who want to use a computer for useful purposes. The Spectrum has some marvellous games software available, but expanding it to perform word processing, for example, results in costs approaching those of the QL.

QL specifications

Let's look at the features that help to make the QL a rival to machines costing much more.

1) A high resolution video display that offers two modes of operation. A UHF socket will feed a domestic monochrome or colour television, while a monitor socket provides feeds of both composite video and RGB signals to drive high quality monitors. The two modes are therefore designed for each type of display.

   The 256 (low) mode should suit all televisions. The horizontal resolution is 256 pixels, which is to say that the width of the display is made up of 256 discrete points. The vertical resolution is also 256, so the display consists of a grid of 256 × 256 dots (65,536), each of which can be one of eight colours; a hardware-generated flash can also be produced in this mode. 20 lines of 37 characters are normally displayed.

   The 512 (high) mode is intended only for use with a monitor, although a high quality TV may be adequate for text, if not colour. In this mode, the horizontal resolution is increased to 512 pixels, the vertical resolution remaining at 256. The number of colours is restricted to four — black, red, green and white — although stipple patterns can produce other colourings; there is no flash. With a monitor it is possible to squeeze up to 25 lines of 85 characters on to the screen.

2) A 'real' keyboard that allows touch typing. A software buffer ensures that the computer can keep up with the fastest typist. There is a full-size space bar plus five function keys.

3) A BASIC interpreter that allows the use of procedures and functions, and encourages good programming practices with its control structures. The single-key entry system used by previous Sinclair computers has been abandoned, but syntax checking of new lines has been retained. However, the ability to spell is important as, for example, the word PRUNT will be taken to be a procedure name. Overall, the dialect is for users who want an elegant, structured language rather than one which is either quick to learn or run.

4) The provision of QDOS, an operating system which is not only used by SuperBASIC but can be used by application programs to perform the necessary housekeeping, input and output tasks. QDOS ensures that machine code programs can use the ROM routines, even if these are relocated in later versions of the QL. Note that programs do not run 'under' QDOS, as with other systems — QDOS is there to perform tasks for programs. The operating system also allows machine code programs to run with a certain degree of 'concurrency'. Two or more routines can be executed simultaneously — or, to be strictly accurate, each routine is allowed a certain slice of the processor's time.

5) Two built-in microdrives, each capable of storing over 100K of programs, data or machine code on a cartridge. Although very similar to Spectrum microdrives, they have slightly more capacity, so that the two systems are not compatible. The performance approximates to floppy disk drives — in comparison to cassette storage, they are a joy to use.

6) 128K of random access memory, of which over 90K is available for programs and data. The 68008's 20-bit address bus allows this large quantity of memory to be available without resorting to any form of 'bank switching', as required when, for example, a Z80 hosts more than 64K of RAM.

7) A dual port serial interface conforming to RS232 standards. The use of printers (with serial interfaces) and networks is therefore possible.

8) A BEEP sound-generating mechanism. Unlike the Spectrum, the QL can continue to compute whilst making a noise!

9) A real-time clock, from which SuperBASIC can decode the day, month and year. The promise of a battery back-up was not fulfilled, so the clock must be reset after the QL has been switched on.

10) Two expansion sockets. The ROM socket at the back of the machine can host a 16K plug-in cartridge, while the larger socket at the lefthand end provides all the necessary signals for any major expansion.

11) Four software packages covering the main requirements of business users. These programs give the QL credibility as a 'serious' user's machine, and allow purchasers to get the QL working for them without having to program the machine themselves.

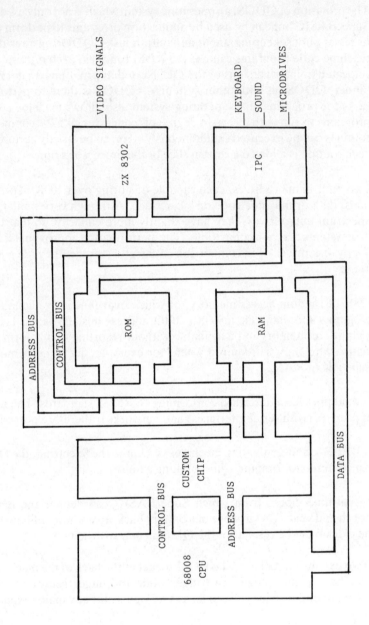

Figure 5.1: QL Hardware

The appeal of the QL will be, for many people, the last point listed above (although it is outside the scope of this book). Adding a printer and colour monitor completes a system which compares with many office computers, at a bargain price.

The power of the raw machine, with its advanced CPU, SuperBASIC and display, gives computer hobbyists good reason to show interest in the QL.

Hardware structure

The structure of the hardware of the Sinclair QL is represented in **Figure 5.1**. If you were to compare this with the actual circuit board inside the case, there would not at first appear to be any resemblance; yet, apart from some small components that cloud the picture, the main features can be identified. On the far left is the CPU itself, a 68008-L8, the L8 defining the clock speed at which the microprocessor is capable of running. An eight-bit data bus runs round the board from the CPU to the other main components, occasionally being buffered from conflicts by appropriate resistors and diodes. The full 20-bit address bus does not reach all areas, some decoding being carried out to eliminate unnecessary signals (memory decoding circuits process the address lines to eliminate unnecessary signals and generate other signals).

At the right of the board, beside the microdrive assemblies, is the second processor, the IPC, an 8049 chip that contains its own RAM and ROM areas, separate from the main memory map. Most input and output handling is performed by this chip, and we will examine it in more detail in Chapter 11.

Two other large chips, each with 40 pins, are also very obvious. One, marked custom chip, is next to the 68008, and is mainly concerned with decoding memory addresses. The other, marked ZX8302 (also known as the video chip or master chip) lives near the 8049, and is concerned with creating the video display, amongst other things. Both these integrated circuits are custom-built for the QL — there is nothing 'magical' inside them. Their roles could be undertaken by a collection of logic chips, although the space these would occupy might demand a huge circuit board: the factors of size and cost work to the advantage of custom-built chips. Found in close proximity to the ZX8302 are some 'crystals' (not shown in the diagram). These are the external components of the oscillator circuits within the chip, which generate clock signals and other high frequency signals required to produce a video display.

The ROM chips are the next most prominent components, and are sited in front of the serial and joystick sockets. There are two chips, one with 32K capacity, the other with 16K. These read only memories contain all the resident machine code that provides both QDOS and Super-BASIC.

Beneath the ROMs are a clutch of RAM chips, 16 in all. These each have a capacity of 64K *bits* of data, that is to say they contain 65,536 individual memory cells. Together, these dynamic random access memory chips make up the impressive 128K of memory at the QL's disposal.

Feeding a domestic television requires a good deal of electronics. The colour and luminance signals must be coded into a composite video signal, and also 'modulated'. As you know, different TV stations broadcast on different channels: the QL, in common with most computers, transmits on channel 36. The modulating circuitry, enclosed in a metal screening box (or 'can') is behind the lefthand microdrive.

Most of the remaining components are concerned either with buffering the various signals between the major areas of the circuit board and connectors, or with providing the correct supply voltages without which the integrated circuits could not function. The voltages which are supplied by the external mains adaptor are 9 volts d.c. and an alternating voltage of around 15 volts. The majority of the chips require 5 volts to work, and any more would cause damage: this is derived from the raw 9 volts. A voltage regulator smooths out the bumps and lowers the voltage to one suitable for the chips; the large metal heatsink behind the microdrives dissipates the surplus in the form of heat (which, you may notice, nicely warms the righthand side of the case!). Other special requirements include plus and minus 12 volts for the RAM chips — this is generated from the a.c. supplied by the mains adaptor.

A word of advice for the incurably inquisitive amongst you. If you take your machine apart to investigate inside, you will almost certainly invalidate any guarantee that the makers or suppliers offer, but you are unlikely to do any damage, *if* you take care. Wait for the warranty to expire if you can possibly contain yourself.

The two halves of the case are held together by eight cross-headed screws. Having removed the power and any other leads, remove the screws. All are located under the case: four short screws along the front lip beneath the keyboard, the remaining four along the back. Don't remove the two screws beneath the microdrive slots, as they hold the drives in place. Now turn the machine the correct way up and lift off the top. Be gentle! The keyboard is connected to the lower part by two *very* fragile ribbon cables. If these do come out of their sockets, reinsert them very carefully, taking great care not to kink them — they will bend all too easily and may fracture. Snoop away to your heart's content, but when you put it back together, don't leave anything extraneous inside!

CHAPTER 6
At the Heart of the QL: the 68008

Your Sinclair QL contains a Motorola 68008 microprocessor, which is a member of the 68000 family. These CPUs are widely thought to be the most powerful design of the 16-bit generation of processors. Although the 68008 shares the same internal architecture as the 68000, and the machine code is identical, the 68008 only possesses an eight-bit data bus. This makes it cheaper, more compact, and easier to interface with widely available support chips: but at the expense of reducing operating speed. By the standards of conventional eight-bit chips, however, it is still fast.

External connections
Your QL's CPU has 48 pins: conventional eight-bit processors such as the Zilog Z80 normally have 40, while full 16-bit CPUs such as the 68000 boast up to 64. As with the model CPU which we looked at in Section 1 of this book, the pins fall into four main groups.

Supply connections: The power supply to make the CPU function must be provided as a voltage difference of +5 volts between the Vcc pin and the two GND pins. The other essential requirement is for a clock signal: this must be a TTL level square wave signal applied to the CLK pin. It can have a frequency of up to 10 megahertz.

Data Bus: The bi-directional pins to connect the CPU to the computer data bus are labelled D0 to D7. The CPU can only send or receive one byte of data at a time — word-sized (ie 16-bit) data operations require the data pins to be used twice, once for each byte.

Address Bus: There are 20 address pins, labelled A0 to A19. This allows 1 megabyte of different addresses to be generated with which to address RAM, ROM or other external devices. The number of pins is one of the advantages of the 68008 over less up-to-date processors, which may only be able to address 64K of memory.

Inside the Sinclair QL

Control Bus: Control signals to and from other hardware devices are passed through a number of control pins. The functions of these pins are many and varied, and deserve a fuller description.

While all four of the above groups of pins closely follow the functions of our model CPU from Section 1, the control pins are much more complex than the simple RD and WR pins described earlier. They fall into six categories.

Asynchronous bus control

Two pins are used to signal to other circuits that the address and data bus pins are active. If AS (Address Strobe) is active, this shows that the address bus pins are sending a valid address to the computer's address bus. DS (Data Strobe) indicates one of two states when it is active — either the data pins are sending a valid byte, or they are waiting to receive one. Which of these is the case depends on a third pin, R/W (Read/Write). If this is held high, then the CPU wishes to read in data from the data bus: if it is pulled low, then it is attempting to write the data on its data pins to memory. In both cases, the target memory location is that which is currently on the address pins.

The pin which gives the name 'asynchronous' to this form of bus control is called DTACK, meaning Data Transfer ACKnowledge. The CPU waits until the memory or peripheral circuits assert the DTACK line before assuming that the circuit has responded. This is the beauty of having an asynchronous bus control system — unlike synchronous methods, external hardware does not have to react within a certain number of clock cycles, so the speed of the computer does not need to be 'designed down' to the response time of its slower components. This is particularly useful for attaching peripheral circuits such as I/O chips which may have a variable response time.

A read cycle performed by the asynchronous bus control method goes through the following steps. On the first clock cycle the address required to be read is placed on the address bus, and then the AS and DS pins are asserted. On the next cycle the CPU checks the DTACK pin: if it has been asserted, two clock cycles pass while the value on the data bus is transferred into the processor. If DTACK had not been asserted by the second clock pulse, the CPU would wait, checking DTACK on each pulse until it became active, before proceeding with the read. So the DTACK pin gives external memory and other circuits the chance to say to the CPU, 'Hang on, I'm not ready yet'.

Note that I have used the word 'asserted' to indicate that DS, AS and DTACK are active — these pins, in common with the rest of the control bus, are active low, and are at logic level zero when asserted.

62

Synchronous bus control

To allow the 68008 to be interfaced with certain peripheral chips (notably the 6800 series of hardware devices that accompanied Motorola's earlier eight-bit CPU, the 6800) two extra pins are provided. By using these pins, devices need not signal back to the CPU that they are ready: it is assumed that they will respond within four clock cycles.

The E, or enable, pin sends out a signal that has a tenth of the frequency of the main clock, but the E cycle is not symmetrical, spending six clock cycles low and then four high. The VPA pin (Valid Peripheral Address) is used to signal to the CPU that it is sending an address which is wired up for synchronous control.

Let us follow a read cycle that invokes the E and VPA pins. The CPU places an address and data on the appropriate buses and then asserts AS and DS; to signal that it wishes to read, it pulls the R/W pin high. External circuits may now examine the address and find that the desired location hosts a device that should use synchronous bus control; if this is the case the circuits pull the VPA pin low. The CPU recognises this, and ignores the DTACK pin — it now knows it will receive the data in sync with the pulses on its E pin. The data pins are enabled on the next positive-going pulse of the E clock: by the time that a negative-going E pulse is sensed, the peripheral circuit will have placed a valid byte of data on the bus, and the read operation is complete.

Bus arbitration

Two pins of the 68000 are provided to allow for complex hardware design. In certain types of computer design, it may be desirable to allow another device, perhaps even another processor, to take control of the address and data bus so that it may use the computer's memory or other peripherals. The BR (Bus Request) pin can be used to force the 68008 to relinquish control over the buses. BG (Bus Grant) is used by the CPU to signal that it has ceased to use the buses.

Interrupt pins

These alter the behaviour of the processor, halting operations and causing an 'exception' to occur. These are handled by software, and we will look at them in detail later in this chapter. There are two interrupt pins, IPL0/2 and IPL1. Note that the 68000 CPU has three, (IPL0, 1 and 2), but, in order to keep the number of pins down, the 68008 combines IPL0 and IPL1.

Signalling the state of the CPU

Three pins, FC0, FC1 and FC2 give out signals that indicate what type of operation the processor is currently attempting. For example, it is possible for external hardware to detect if the CPU is fetching a program instruction, that is, using the PC to collect information. Although the QL does not make use of this facility, it would be possible to provide overlapping blocks of memory, one containing a program in ROM and the other holding data in RAM, but both using the same addresses.

System control
BERR, the Bus ERRor pin, gives the hardware designer the chance to recover from a minor hardware fault. If, for example, external memory fails to assert the DTACK pin, a watchdog timer circuit could force this pin low after a suitable period of time: the result would be an exception similar to one caused by an interrupt.

The two final pins, HALT and RESET, can either work as a team or separately. If both are pulled low by external hardware for more than a tenth of a second, they will cause the CPU to perform a 'power on' reset similar to the reset of our model computer in Section 1. What actually occurs is a special sort of exception. Individually, the HALT pin can be used to pause the operation of the CPU; while RESET, which is a bi-directional pin, can be asserted by software in order to reset other external hardware.

Inside the 68008
Having taken a look at the outside of the chip, let's now take a look inside. There is no need to examine the actual circuitry. The structure of the control unit, ALU, internal buses and registers is the same as that we looked at in Chapter 3, albeit in an extended and advanced form. What we will examine is what is known as a programmer's model, a simplified version of the chip.

The 68008 is equipped with no less than 18 32-bit registers and one 16-bit register. There are eight data registers, numbered D0 to D7: these are 32 bits in length, but byte-size operations are carried out by using the low eight bits, word-size operations use bits 0 to 15, and long word operations use all 32 bits (see Chapter 2). The next eight registers are the address registers, A0 to A7 — again, 32 bits in length, but not usable for byte operations, only word and long word. Address register 7 has special properties — it acts as the 'user stack pointer' (USP).

The advantage of the distinction between address and data registers is to allow different rules to apply. For example, adding a value to a data register will affect the flags (condition codes), but adding a value to an address register will not. This does *not* mean that you cannot store (or manipulate) a value you intend to use as an address in a data register, but in order to use it as an address it will be far easier to transfer it into an address register. 16 registers should be more than adequate for most purposes, so it does no harm to restrict their flexibility a little. The benefits are great, as programming becomes more consistent, and the condition codes always react in the most useful way.

The last two 32-bit registers are the 'supervisor stack pointer' (SSP) — I will explain the reason for two stack pointers when we get on to the subject of operating modes — and the program counter.

The 16-bit status register has two halves — the low byte holds the condition codes (or flags), and the high byte holds information as to the status of the microprocessor (we will discuss this in a moment).

Before we look at the machine code instructions available to the user (in the next chapter), it is worth covering the subjects of processing states, operating modes and exceptions.

Processing states

There are three possible processing states that the 68008 can assume. The least interesting, from our point of view, is the HALTed state. If, for example, a bus error has occurred (ie BERR has been pulled low), and while the CPU is dealing with it another bus error occurs, the processor gives up, assuming that there is something seriously wrong with its surrounding hardware. The processor enters the halted state, effectively frozen, and nothing will happen until a RESET is received.

The two main processing states are normal (the state in which most processing occurs) and exception (when the CPU is handling events such as a reset or the interrupts mentioned earlier), and these are covered in the next two sections.

Operating modes

There are two types of normal state: the 68008 can operate in either 'supervisor' mode or 'user' mode. The provision of two levels allows programs which run in supervisor mode to oversee the running of the computer, while the lower privilege user mode is restricted from interfering with some aspects of the system. This facility is intended mainly for the separation of software, for example, providing protection of the operating system from user programs and so allowing multi-tasking.

In supervisor mode, the CPU can access all 16 bits of the status register. The high byte is called the 'system byte'. Bits 8, 9 and 10 provide an interrupt mask which is used when the CPU receives an interrupt signal, one of the events which cause a switch to the exception state. Bits 11, 12 and 14 are not used. Bit 13 is important: this is the supervisor bit (the S bit) which indicates which mode the CPU is in. Bit 15 provides a trace facility — the 68008 has circuitry which allows the execution of a program one instruction at a time, with a diversion to a user-written debugging program after each step. The lower byte, called the 'user byte', contains the condition codes carry, overflow, zero, negative and extend in bits 0 to 4 respectively (bits 5–7 are not used). This user byte is known as the condition code register, or CCR, when referred to on its own.

So what differences are there between the two modes? When the S bit is set, the 68008 is in supervisor mode, all machine code instructions are available, and the SSP register (referred to as A7') is used by the CPU as the stack pointer. In addition, signals from the FC pins can be used by external memory to detect that the chip is in supervisor mode. When in supervisor mode, the CPU could find a different memory device at a particular location than that present in user mode, although this facility is not implemented on the QL.

When in user mode, apart from the different hardware signals generated, the USP (A7) is used as the stack pointer and there are limitations imposed on the instruction set.

A group of instructions, known as 'privileged', will not operate in user mode — trying to execute one of them will cause an exception, the CPU will switch into supervisor mode and jump to a routine to handle this 'error'. All the privileged instructions are system control operations; and any instruction that can alter the status register, and therefore the system byte, is privileged, so in user mode it is impossible to switch on the trace or supervisor bit, or alter the interrupt mask. It is still possible to read the system byte, and the condition codes may be altered with instructions that refer only to the CCR. An instruction used at the end of exception processing, RTE (return from exception), is privileged because, as we will see in a moment, exceptions are always processed by the CPU in the supervisor state. In user mode it is also illegal to try and send out a RESET signal or STOP the processor. The last privileged instruction is MOVE USP, which alters the contents of the user stack pointer.

In supervisor mode, register A7' is used as the stack pointer and, before switching to a user mode program, the main program may want to set up a stack for that user program. In order to achieve this, register A7, the USP, needs to be altered to point to the user stack. Trying to move data into A7 will result in changing A7' as the S bit is set, so a special instruction is provided. However, in user mode, A7' cannot be altered, as a user program able to move the stack of the supervisor program stack would cause chaos. A user program has no need of MOVE USP as it may use MOVE to A7, so any program that contains MOVE USP is either not a user program or is doing something silly.

To summarise these differences between user and supervisor modes, hardware signals can be decoded externally to distinguish between them.

Also, user mode cannot STOP, RESET or process an exception, and it cannot change the contents of the SSP or the system byte of the status register.

Exceptions

Exceptions have been mentioned a number of times now. The term is used to describe a number of events that occur for differing reasons, but all these events divert the processor from its current program to execute a portion of code to handle the exception. Often, on completion of this task, the CPU will be returned to the point where it left off.

The most fundamental exception is Reset, which occurs when the RESET and HALT pins of the CPU are pulled low by external circuitry for longer than one tenth of a second. Reset is intended to initialise the CPU and computer after the power has been turned on, or to rescue the system from a 'crash'; it therefore does not need to remember what the CPU was doing before the reset signal was received. When the reset signal is recognised, the CPU goes into the exception state: the S bit is set to put the CPU into supervisor mode, and the trace bit is reset to zero, in case it was previously set. A memory fetch cycle commences on the next clock pulse. The CPU needs to know two pieces of information — a starting value for both the SSP and PC — and it will fetch these from locations 0–7, part of an area of memory set aside to hold the exception vectors — each vector is a long word address (each has four locations). Between addresses 0 and 3FFh, the 68008 needs to find a table of values it can use as addresses for the processing of exceptions. The hardware surrounding the CPU must therefore provide memory at these locations and these are stored in ROM: when the computer is started up, any RAM contents would be meaningless. The processor, using four fetch cycles, collects the bytes from locations 0, 1, 2 and 3 (vector 0) and places this long word of data into A7, the SSP: it then repeats the process, taking the long word from addresses 4 to 7 (vector 1), and places this in the program counter. Therefore the ROM must contain, at addresses 0 through to 3, the top address for the supervisor stack the system is to use and, at addresses 4 through to 7, the address that we wish the CPU to jump to when it is reset.

Note that each exception vector takes up four bytes of memory. The PC is 32 bits long and is therefore loaded with a 32-bit value even though only the low 20 bits will be used.

To summarise what happens after a Reset, the CPU enters the supervisor state, loads the SSP with the address held in exception vector 0, and then loads the PC with the address held in vector 1; this causes a jump to the system software that sets up the computer.

Now let's examine the rest of the exceptions in their order of vector numbers — only a brief outline is given at this point, exceptions that are used by the QL will be expanded on later. All exception processing begins with the same set of operations. A temporary copy is made internally of the status register (SR), the S bit is set and the T bit reset. The vector number is generated internally and multiplied by four (by shifting it two bits to the right) to determine the address of the vector. The PC (pointing to the next instruction to be processed) and the temporary copy of the contents of the SR is pushed on to the supervisor stack. It is at this point that the exceptions start to vary — some may save further information before fetching the address to jump to from the vector table.

We have already covered vectors 0 and 1 (RESET).

Bus error (vector 2) is the response to the BERR pin being asserted by external circuitry: this indicates that a read or write operation has failed. In order to have sufficient information to try and rerun the operation, the following are all saved on the stack — the instruction in the instruction register, the address that the CPU was attempting to access, the function code present on the FC pins, and flags to indicate if a read or write was being performed and if an instruction was being executed.

The address in vector 2 points the CPU to software that may use the information placed on the stack to salvage the situation if it can.

Address error (v3) is similar to bus error. It occurs if the CPU tries to access information that is a word or long word, starting at an odd numbered address. Only bytes may be written to or read from odd addresses — you are not allowed to store word information starting at address 4001h, for example. It also follows that instructions which are 16 bits, or multiples of 16, must start at even addresses.

Illegal instruction (v4) is used to respond to bit patterns that do not correspond to any recognised instruction. This might happen if code is assembled by hand (or with a faulty assembler program!), or if a jump is performed to a section of memory that contains not program code but data of some description. There is a special code, 'illegal', to force this exception deliberately.

Zero divide (v5) will occur if you ask the CPU to divide a number by zero, using the DIVU or DIVS instructions.

CHK (v6) is a response to a machine code instruction, 'check register against bounds', which compares a data register against a two's complement operand (operand meaning the value supplied by instruction, using one of the addressing modes). If the register contains a two's complement number that is negative or greater than the operand, this exception is processed.

TRAPV (v7) is another software-generated exception; when the 'trap on overflow' instruction is encountered, an exception begins if the V (over-flow) condition code is set.

Privilege violation (v8) will occur if the CPU meets, while in user mode, an instruction intended for use only in supervisor mode.

Trace (v9) is used in conjunction with the T bit of the SR: if this is set then a jump to an exception routine especially written to handle the tracing and debugging of programs will be made after each instruction. In this way, the operation of a program can be investigated one step at a time.

1010 (v10) allows the simulation of instructions that do not exist in the 68008 instruction set, but may be introduced on more advanced proces-sors in the 68000 family. Codes with 1010 as their first four bits are called unimplemented, rather than illegal, instructions — if a 68008 encounters one it begins exception processing, and software may be able to react accordingly. Vector 10 may also be used for user-defined instructions.

1111 (v11) is another vector for unimplemented instructions, in this case beginning with the bit pattern 1111.

Vectors 12 to 23 consist of exceptions of little interest to users of the 68008: they are for events that should not occur or are reserved for future expansion by Motorola.

Spurious interrupt (v24) is the first of the interrupt vectors, which will be discussed in a moment.

Auto interrupt vectors (v25 to v31) are also part of the interrupt system.

Traps (v32 to v47) are software-induced exceptions. The TRAP instruc-tion supplies one of the 16 values which dictate which vector is used. They can be used to allow user programs to make quick, vectored calls to the operating system.

Vectors 48 to 63 are further, unassigned locations reserved by Motorola.

User interrupt vectors (v64 to v255) contain the addresses relating to user interrupts.

Interrupts

The interrupt system of the 68008 is flexible yet complex. The QL uses only one type of interrupt, the auto vectored type, although we will also look at two other types — user interrupts and spurious interrupts.

An interrupt is an exception which is caused by external hardware: a program which is running when an interrupt signal is received will eventually be allowed to recommence — interrupts tend to inform the CPU that the keyboard, serial ports or other devices have some information for processing: they also allow the time-sharing aspects of a multi-tasking system to be implemented.

The 68008 has a slightly strange interrupt system, mainly because it is a cut down version of that available on the 68000 CPU, which is equipped with three, rather than the 68008's two, interrupt pins. Before describing the 68008, consider a CPU that has three pins, IPL0, IPL1 and IPL2: by asserting a combination of these pins, external hardware can send a total of seven different signals to the CPU. The method is pure binary: if none of the pins is asserted, there is no interrupt signal; IPL0 asserted gives a value of 1, IPL1 a value of 2 and IPL2 a value of 4. From this you can see that if external hardware pulls IPL0 and IPL2 low (makes them active), the value 5 is placed on the interrupt pins.

We can consider the pins as a small, three-bit interrupt bus, capable of asking for one of seven levels of exception processing. To give the CPU some control over the interrupts, there is a system provided that allows the software to set a level below which these interrupts will be ignored. A three-bit mask is contained in the status register, which can be set to one of eight values. If the mask contains 0, then any interrupt will be acknowledged: if the mask is set to 3, for example, then only interrupts that place a higher value than 3 on the IPL pins will have any effect. Once an interrupt has been accepted, the mask is set to that level of priority, so only interrupts of a higher value can divert the CPU's attention with an exception. The only interrupt signal that the CPU cannot ignore is a level 7 signal, whatever the state of the mask — this is known as a 'non-maskable' interrupt.

We now return to the 68008: it has only two IPL pins, one of which has the value 2 (IPL1); the other is IPL0 and IPL2 combined, and therefore has the value 5. External hardware can signal one of four states to the CPU through the interrupt pins — no interrupt, level 2, level 5 and level 7 (ie both pins asserted).

How does the CPU decide which vector to use for its exception processing? Once it has received a signal which it accepts — level 7 in all circumstances, or either of the other signals if the mask in the SR is set to a lower value — the CPU responds by setting all three of its FC pins high. This will only occur when an exception has been accepted.

Once the external interrupting hardware has been informed that its interrupt has been accepted, it must reply with a signal to tell the CPU which type of interrupt it is — auto, user or spurious. If it requires an auto vector to be used, it must assert the CPU's VPA pin. If this is the case, the table of addresses v25 to v31 are used — a level 2 interrupt (IPL0/2 off, IPL1 on) uses v26; level 5 (IPL0/2 on, IPL1 off) uses v29; while the level 7 exception address comes from v31. Note that the other auto vectors cannot be used on the 68008 — it has insufficient pins to generate their level values.

User interrupts follow the same pattern in terms of priority, but when the interrupting device detects the 'interrupt accepted' signal on the FC pins, it must do two things. It asserts the DTACK pin to tell the CPU that it is a user interrupt, and it places a user vector number on the data bus. Vector addresses v64 to v255 are reserved for these user interrupts, although any vector number could be placed on the data bus to be used by the exception.

The third type of interrupt is designed to allow for system errors. If BERR is asserted in response to the FC signal, then the CPU deems the interrupt to be 'spurious' and uses v24 as the vector number. In this location it expects to find the address of an exception handling software routine that will cope with the error.

The occurrence of an interrupt can be treated as a dialogue between the CPU and the interrupting hardware:

IPL0/2 asserted by the hardware — 'I am a level 5 interrupting device and require servicing'.

FC pins pulled high by the CPU — 'Your priority is sufficiently high for me to deal with you: what type of interrupt are you?'

If the hardware responds by asserting VPA — 'I require you to use an auto vector' — the CPU will use v29.

If the hardware asserts DTACK, 'I want you to use a user interrupt vector, the number of which I have placed on the data bus'.

If the hardware asserts BERR — 'What interrupt? No one out here sent an interrupt! Use vector 24'.

This chapter has given a picture of the hardware facilities the 68008 provides; what can be done with them relies on the software instructions we will meet in the next chapter.

CHAPTER 7
Talking to the CPU:
the 68008 Instruction Set

This chapter is not intended to be read in a linear manner. It is arranged in alphabetical order so that it can be used for reference. For a gentle introduction to the instruction set, study the most common instruction, MOVE, first, followed by simple arithmetic, branch and stack instructions. Note that the descriptions assume that you have read the MOVE description first, as this fully explains the abbreviations used. The opcode is normally given as a 16-bit word; if a bit is represented as a letter, the meaning is given in the text. When an instruction has only one form, its hex value is shown; otherwise examples are given where appropriate.

Finally, don't try to wade through this chapter in one go: later chapters give simple examples of machine code routines, and these should be looked at to get the 'feel' of the instruction set in use.

ABCD

Add Binary-Coded Decimal: this operation adds the source to the destination, adding a further 1 if the extend bit is set, using the rules of BCD (see Chapter 2). There are two addressing modes available, both of which operate on only byte-sized data. You may ABCD the contents of one data register to another; or ABCD a byte pointed to by one address register to another, also pointed to by an address register. The two registers are used in the predecrement mode, that is, they have 1 subtracted from them before being used as pointers.

Syntax:	ABCD Dy,Dx *or* ABCD $-$(Ay),$-$(Ax)
Opcode:	1100xxx10000myyy
	x is the number of the destination register
	m determines which addressing mode is used:
	if m=0 the mode is data register direct, if m=1 the mode is address register indirect with predecrement
	y is the number of the source register
Example:	CB0Eh = ABCD $-$(A6),$-$(A5): decrement A6 and A5, then ABCD the byte pointed to by A6 and the extend flag, or X bit to that pointed to by A5

Flags: *Z* cleared if the result is non-zero, else unchanged
                             C set if a decimal carry occurs, else cleared
                             X as for C
                             N and *V* are undefined

ADD

The binary ADDition instruction. A data register must be used as either the source or the destination; the other operand may use any of the available addressing modes if it is the source, or one of the following if it is the destination: (An), (An)+, −(An), d(An), d(An,ix), Abs.W, Abs.L (see MOVE for definitions).

Syntax: ADD <ea>,Dn (data register is destination), *or*
                      ADD Dn,<ea> (effective address is destination)

Opcode: 1101nnnmssaaarrr
                      n is the number of the data register
                      m determines the direction of the operation:
                      if m=0 then the data register is the destination, if m=1 then the data register is the source
                      s is the size of the operation:
                      00 = byte, 01= word, 10 = long word
                      a is the effective addressing mode (see MOVE)
                      r is the effective addressing register (see MOVE)

Example: D211h = ADD.B (A1),D1; add the byte pointed to by A1 to the low byte of D1

Flags: the condition codes are all affected as normal

ADDA

Binary ADDition using an Address register as the destination. Similar to ADD, but operation restricted to word and long word size and, as an aid to programming, the condition codes are not altered. The source may use any addressing mode.

Syntax: ADD <ea>, An

Opcode: 1101nnns11aaarrr
                      n is the number of the address register
                      s is the size of the operation:
                      0 = word, 1= long word
                      a is the effective addressing mode (see MOVE)

	r is the effective addressing register (see MOVE)
Flags:	unaffected

ADDI

This instruction allows the ADDition of Immediate data, included in the next word or two words of program, to destinations addressed by the fol-lowing modes: Dn, (An), (An)+, −(An), d(An), d(An,xi), Abs.W, Abs.L. This instruction can operate on all three data sizes. If byte-sized, the immediate data is contained in the low byte of the following program word. If long-word-sized two following program words are required.

Syntax:	ADDI #<data>,<ea>
Opcode:	00000110ssaaarrr + one or two words
	s is the size (see ADD)
	a is the effective addressing mode (see MOVE)
	r is the effective addressing register (see MOVE)
Flags:	all affected as usual

ADDQ

ADD Quick is a fast method of adding a value between 1 and 8 to a des-tination. The data is actually included in the word of the instruction, making it compact as well as speedy. The three bits used for the data rep-resent their binary value, unless they are all zero, in which case the value 8 is implied. All the addressing modes except d(PC), d(PC,ix) and Imm are allowed. All data sizes are available.

Syntax:	ADDQ #<data>,<ea>
Opcode:	0101ddd0ssaaarrr
	d are the three data bits (special case 000=8)
	s is the size (see ADD)
	a is the effective addressing mode (see MOVE)
	r is the effective addressing register
Example:	5601h = ADDQ.B #3,D1; add 3 to the low byte of D1
Flags:	affected as usual unless the destination is an address register, in which case unchanged

ADDX

Performs a binary ADDition, including the value of the eXtend bit in the result. The format is the same as ABCD, allowing the source and destination to be data registers or address register indirect with predecrement.

Syntax: ADDX Dy,Dx *or* ADDX −(Ay),−(Ax)

Opcode: 1101xxx1ss00myyy
x is the number of the source register
s is the size (see ADD)
m is the mode:
if m=0 then data registers are the source and destination, if m=1 then source and destination are pointed to by the predecremented address registers
y is the number of the destination register

Flags: all affected as normal except Z, which is cleared if the result is zero, else unchanged

AND

A logical operation that ANDs the source and destination bits together and places the result in the destination. Either the source or the destination must be a data register: if a data register is the destination, then all modes except An can define the source; if a data register is the source, then the destination can only be defined by the addressing modes: (An), (An)+, −(An), d(An), d(An,xi), Abs.W, Abs.L.

Syntax: AND <ea>,Dn *or* AND Dn,<ea>

Opcode: 1100nnnmssaaarrr
n is the data register number
m is the mode:
if m=0 the data register is the destination, if m=1 the data register is the source
s is the size (see ADD)
a is the effective addressing mode (see MOVE)
r is the effective addressing register (see MOVE)

Example: C6A9, 0080h = AND.L 80h(A1),D3; take the long word pointed to by 80h + A1, then AND it with the bits in D3, leaving the result there

Flags: X is unaffected
N and Z react as normal
V and C are always cleared

ANDI

A special AND instruction that deals only with Immediate data, which may be a byte, word or long word. The destination may be addressed by any of the following modes: Dn, (An), (An)+, −(An), d(An), d(An,xi), Abs.W, Abs.L

Syntax: ANDI #<data>,<ea>

Opcode: 00000010ssaaarrr + one or two data words
                     s is the size (see ADD)
                     a is the effective addressing mode (see MOVE)
                     r is the effective addressing register (see MOVE)

Flags: as AND

ANDI to CCR

An instruction to alter the flags by ANDing them with Immediate data, contained in the low five bits of the following word.

Syntax: ANDI #xxx,CCR

Opcode: 0000001000111100 + one word of data
Hex value: 023Ch

Flags: C, V, Z, N and X relate to bits 0 to 4 of data byte
                     Flags are cleared if relative bit is 0, else unchanged.

ANDI to SR

This is a privileged instruction; any attempt to use it in the user mode will cause an exception through vector 8. Similar to ANDI to CCR, it uses 16 bits of immediate data and therefore can change the system byte of the SR.

Syntax: ANDI #xxx, SR

Opcode: 0000001001111100 + one word of data
Hex value: 027Ch

Flags: as ANDI to CCR
                     The same rules apply to the bits of the system byte, where bits 8 to 10 are IO to I2, bit 13 is the S bit and bit 15 is the T bit.

ASL

The letters of this instruction stand for Arithmetic Shift Left. Imagine a 16-bit value in memory. This operation copies bit 15 into the C and X flags, shifts bit 14 into 15, 13 into 14, and so on until bit 0 is copied into bit 1; then a 0 is placed in bit 0. When ASL is applied to memory, the addressing modes (An), (An)+, −(An), d(An), d(An,xi), Abs.W and Abs.L can be used; the instruction then only operates on words of data, and performs a shift of one place as described above. The other form that ASL takes is for operations on data registers: the number of shifts performed is dictated either by a 3-bit value contained in the opcode, or taken from a data register specified by the instruction. When a data register is the destination byte, word or long word shifts can be performed.

Syntax:	ASL Dx,Dy (Dx specifies number of shifts, maximum 64)
	ASL #<data>,Dy (data specifies number of shifts)
	ASL <ea> (one shift only, word size)

Opcodes:

Memory: 1110000111aaarrr

a is the effective addressing mode (sée MOVE)

r is the effective addressing register (see MOVE)

Data register: 1110ccc1ssi00rrr

c is the data specifying the number of shifts (000=8) or the data register number (if i=1)

s is the size (see ADD)

i dictates if data or a register specifies the shift count: if i=0 then c is data, if i=1 then c is a data register containing the count

r is the data destination register number

Example: E322h = ASL.B D1,D2; if D1 contains 3, the low byte of D2 is shifted left arithmetically three times

Flags:

N and *Z* act as normal

V is set if the highest bit is changed at any time, else cleared

C is set to the value of the last bit shifted into it and cleared if no shifts actually occur

X as *C*, but unaffected by a shift count of zero

ASR

All the syntax rules of ASL apply to this instruction, which stands for Arithmetic Shift Right — as the name implies, the opposite direction to

ASL. The least significant bit is shifted into C and X, the other bits are moved to the right, ie bit 1 into bit 0: but the high bit is not changed, retaining its old value.

Syntax: ASR Dx,Dy (Dx specifies number of shifts)
              ASR #<data>,Dy (data specifies number of shifts)
              ASR <ea> (one shift only, word size)

Opcodes:
Memory: 1110000011aaarrr
Data register: 1110ccc0ssi00rrr
              where letters are as ASL

Flags: see ASL

Bcc

This Branch on condition code instruction will cause the PC to be modi-fied by the addition of a two's complement value, which may be byte or word length, causing the CPU to continue executing the program from a new point. The action only occurs if the conditions specified in the instruc-tion are met: the condition code flags are tested and, if they are not set to the necessary values, program execution continues with the next instruc-tion. If the branch is short, the displacement is contained in the low eight bits of the opcode. For a long branch, the low byte of the instruction is zero and the 16-bit displacement is supplied as an extension word. The condition tested may be one of 14, listed below.

Syntax: Bcc <label> or Bcc <displacement>
Opcode: 0110ccccdddddddd (+ one word if d=0)
              c is a 4-bit pattern representing one of the available con-ditions:
              0010   HI: high
              0011   LS: low or same — met if C or Z set
              0100   CC or HS: carry clear/high or same — C clear
              0101   CS or LO: carry set/low — C set
              0110   NE: not equal — Z clear
              0111   EQ: equal — Z set
              1000   VC: overflow clear — V clear
              1001   VS: overflow set — V set
              1010   PL: plus — N clear
              1011   MI: minus — N set
              1100   GE: greater or equal — N and V both set or both
                        clear

1101   LT: less than — *N* set and *V* clear, or *N* clear and
        V set
1110   GT: greater than — as GE but *Z* must also be clear
1111   LE: less or equal — as LT or *Z* set
d is a two's complement 8-bit displacement; or, if zero,
a two's complement 16-bit displacement is contained in
next word

Example: 660Ah = BNE +10; if the Z flag is clear branch 10 bytes
past the next instruction

Flags: the condition codes remain unchanged

BCHG

Test a Bit and CHanGe; one bit is taken from the effective address and
placed in the Z flag, its value inverted and then returned to its original
place. The number of the bit can be defined in two ways: from a data
register or from immediate data. If the effective address, ie the destination, is a data register the bit number may be 0 to 31, otherwise 0 to
7; when the supplied bit number is too large, the appropriate modulus is
taken. For example, if a value between 0 and 7 is required and 17 is
supplied, it is divided by eight and the remainder, 1, is used. When the bit
number is taken from a data register, the form is called Bit Number
Dynamic. If it comes from data, the term used is Bit Number Static. In
both forms, the following addressing modes may be used: Dn, (An),
(An)+, −(An), d(An), d(An,xi), Abs.W, Abs.L.

Syntax: BCHG Dn,<ea> *or* BCHG #xxx,<ea>
Opcodes:
Dynamic: 0000xxx101aaarrr
            x is the number of the data register holding the bit
            number
            a is the effective addressing mode (see MOVE)
            r is the effective addressing register (see MOVE)
Static: 0000100001aaarrr + 00000000bbbbbbbb
            a is the effective addressing mode (see MOVE)
            r is the effective address register (see MOVE)
            b is the bit number
Example: 055Ch = BCHG D2, (A4)+; if D2 held 5, for instance,
            then copy bit 5 of the byte pointed to by A4 into Z, com-
            plement the bit itself and increment A4

Flags: only Z is affected, taking on the value of the bit tested

BCLR

An instruction similar to BCHG, with only one difference: the Bit is CLeaRed rather than complemented. All the other rules apply.

Syntax: BCLR Dn,<ea> *or* BCLR #xxx,<ea>

Opcodes:

Dynamic: 0000xxx110aaarrr

Static: 0000100010aaarrr + 00000000bbbbbbbb
where letters are as BCHG

Flags: as BCHG

BRA

BRanch Always. A branching instruction that always works, regardless of the flags. The displacement of the jump is indicated by the same method as that used for Bcc.

Syntax: BRA <label> *or* Bcc <displacement>

Opcode: 01100000dddddddd (+ one word if d=0)
d is the two's complement 8-bit displacement, or zero if a two's complement 16-bit word is supplied

Flags: unchanged

BSET

Another instruction similar to BCHG, the difference being that instead of the Bit being complemented it is SET. All the other rules apply.

Syntax: BSET Dn,<ea> *or* BSET #xxx,<ea>

Opcodes:

Dynamic: 0000xxx111aaarrr

Static: 0000100011aaarrr + 00000000bbbbbbbb
letters are as BCHG

Flags: as BCHG

BSR

Performs a relative Branch to a SubRoutine, placing the old value of the PC on the stack before calculating its new value. See Bcc for the method of storing the displacement. The instruction can be thought of as two others: MOVE PC,−(SP), BRA (routine).

Syntax: BSR <label> *or* BSR <displacement>

Opcode: 01100001dddddddd (+ one word if d=0)

                 d is the two's complement 8-bit displacement or zero if a two's complement 16-bit word is supplied

Example: 6128h = BSR (+28h): push the address of the next instruction on to the stack and add 28h to the PC, causing a jump

Flags: unchanged

BTST

Again, similar to BCHG. However, although the Z flag copies the Bit TeSTed, the bit itself is unaffected. Otherwise, the same rules as BCHG are enforced.

Syntax: BTST Dn,<ea> *or* BTST #xxx,<ea>

Opcodes:

Dynamic: 0000xxx100aaarrr

Static: 0000100000aaarrr + 00000000bbbbbbbb

                 letters are as BCHG

Flags: as BCHG

CHK

CHecK register against bounds. This operation will start an exception, through vector 6, if the low word in the data register it is checking is less than zero (two's complement convention, ie bit 15 set) or greater than a two's complement value taken via any effective addressing mode, except address register direct.

Syntax: CHK <ea>,Dn

Opcode: 0100xxx110aaarrr

                 x is the number of the data register containing the value to be checked

                 a is the effective addressing mode (see MOVE)

                 r is the effective addressing register (see MOVE)

Example: 4FBCh, 00FFh = CHK #00FF,D7: if the contents of D7 are less than zero or =>0100h, initiate an exception through vector 6

Flags: N is set if the data is less than 0, cleared if greater than the specified bound, else undefined
Z, V and C are undefined
X is unaffected

CLR

The method used to CLeaR all the bits of the destination byte, word or long word. Addressing modes are: Dn, (An), (An)+, −(An), d(An), d(An,ix), Abs.W., Abs.L.

Syntax: CLR <ea>
Opcode: 01000010ssaaarrr
s is the size (see ADD)
a is the effective addressing mode (see ADD)
r is the effective addressing register (see ADD)
Example: 4200h = CLR.B D0: clear the low byte of D0
Flags: Z is always set
N, V and C are always set
X is unchanged

CMP

Used to CoMPare two values, one being in a data register, the other derived using any addressing mode. The value from the specified effective address is subtracted from the value in the data register, but the result is not placed in any destination. However, the flags are affected, allowing conditional instructions to react to the result. All sizes are valid.

Syntax: CMP <ea>,Dn
Opcode: 1011xxx0ssaaarrr
x is the data register number
s is the size (see ADD)
a is the effective addressing mode (see ADD)
r is the effective addressing register (see ADD)
Example: B449h = CMP.W A1,D2: subtract the low word in A1 from that in D2, setting the flags but discarding the result. (*Note:* As an address register direct is the effec-

83

tive address, a byte-sized operation would not be allowed: see MOVE.)

Flags: set as normal, except *X*, which is unchanged

CMPA

An instruction that is a variation of CMP; the difference is that an Address register supplies the value which has the data subtracted from it. Because an address register direct is involved, byte size is not allowed.

Syntax: CMPA <ea>,An
Opcode: 1011xxxs11aaarrr
x is the address register number
s is the size:
if s=0 then size = word, if s=1 then size = long word
a is the effective addressing mode (see MOVE)
r is the effective address register (see MOVE)
Flags: as CMP

CMPI

Another version of CMP: a value supplied as Immediate data is subtracted from one supplied using one of the following addressing modes: Dn, (An), (An)+, −(An), d(An), d(An,ix), Abs.W., Abs.L. The flags are set and the result discarded. Any data size can be used.

Syntax: CMPI #<data>,<ea>
Opcode: 00001100ssaaarrr
s is the size (see ADD)
a is the effective addressing mode (see ADD)
r is the effective addressing register (see ADD)
Flags: as CMP

CMPM

This instruction CoMPares two values, both in Memory and pointed to by address registers. To assist searching operations, both registers are used in the post-increment mode. The actual comparison follows the same pattern as CMP.

84

Syntax:	CMPM (Ay)+, (Ax)+
Opcode:	1011xxx1ss001yyy
	x and *y* are address register numbers
	s is size (see ADD)
Example:	D70Ch = CMPM.B (A4)+, (A3)+: compare the byte at
	A4 with that at A3, then increment both registers
Flags:	as CMP

DBcc

Test condition, Decrement and Branch on condition code. This instruction adds the facility of a loop counter to the basic Bcc code. First, the
flags are tested to see if the specified condition is met. If it is, the whole
instruction fails and the CPU passes on to the next instruction (note that
this is the opposite to Bcc). Otherwise, the next step is to decrement the
low word of the data register specified by the code. This is then tested to
check if it contains FFFFh (-1 in two's complement numbering); if it does,
no further action occurs. However, if the data register now contains any
other value, a relative branching operation is performed; the extension
word is added (two's complement style) to the PC, forcing a jump. In
addition to the conditions available for Bcc, DBcc can use the conditions
T (true), which always fails the first test (so it's not very useful!), and F
(false), which always passes, providing a useful instruction that performs
the decrement and branch part of the instruction only (DBF, sometimes
allowed by assemblers as DBRA).

Syntax:	DBcc Dn,<label> *or* DBcc Dn,<displacement>
Opcode:	0101cccc11001xxx
	c is the condition (see Bcc *plus*):
	0001 = false
	0000 = true
	x is the data register number
Example:	56C9h, FFFAh = DBNE D1,−6: if Z is set, subtract 1
	from D1. If that does not result in −1, perform a branch
	of −6
Flags:	not changed

DIVS

Division Signed. One of the most powerful instructions, although it does
take at least 162 clock cycles to perform (it is still quicker than using a

program). The destination is a word held in a data register; the source can have any effective address other than An. The destination word is divided by the source word, using signed arithmetic, the result placed in the low word of the data register and the remainder stored in the high word. If the remainder will not fit into the 16 bits provided, the original values are retained and the V flag set. In addition, if you attempt to divide a number by zero, an exception trap occurs through vector 5.

Syntax:	DIVS <ea>,Dn
Opcode:	1000xxx111aaarrr
	x is the data register number
	a is the effective addressing mode (see MOVE)
	r is the effective addressing register (see MOVE)
Example:	85C1h = DIVS D1,D2: divide the word in D2 by the word in D1, using signed arithmetic. Place the quotient in the low word and the remainder in the high word of D2
Flags:	*N, Z* and *V* affected as usual
	C cleared
	X unaffected

DIVU

DIVide Unsigned. A version of DIVS that does not employ two's complement arithmetic. Otherwise the same.

Syntax:	DIVU <ea>,Dn
Opcode:	1000xxx011aaarrr
	letters are as DIVS
Flags:	as DIVS

EOR

A logical instruction that compares bytes, word, or long word on a bit by bit basis; the result is determined by applying the rules of Exclusive OR. If both bits are the same, a zero results, but if different, the result is 1. The source must be a data register; the destination an effective address from the following list: Dn, (An), (An)+, −(An), d(An), d(An,ix), ABS.W., Abs.L.

Syntax:	EOR Dn,<ea>

Opcode:	1011xxx1ssaaarrr
	x is the data register number
	s is the size (see ADD)
	a is the effective addressing mode (see MOVE)
	r is the effective addressing register (see MOVE)
Example:	B302h = EOR.B D1,D2: if the low byte of D1 contains 01010101 bin and the low byte of D2 contains 01011010 bin, the result in D2 will be 00001111 bin
Flags:	as AND

EORI

An immediate version of EOR, in the same mould as ANDI.

Syntax:	EORI #<data>,<ea>
Opcode:	00001010ssaaarrr + word or words
	s is the size (see ADD)
	a is the effective addressing mode (see ADD)
	r is the effective addressing register (see ADD)
Flags:	as AND

EORI to CCR

An EOR version of ANDI to CCR.

Syntax:	EORI #xxx,CCR
Opcode:	0000101000111100 + word containing data in low byte
Hex value:	0A3Ch + word
Flags:	see ANDI to CCR

EORI to SR

The EOR version of ANDI to SR.

Syntax:	EORI #xxx,SR
Opcode:	0000101001111100 + word
Hex value:	0A7Ch + word
Flags:	see ANDI to SR

EXG

EXchanGe registers. Swap the contents of two registers, either data to data, address to address, or data to address. Only the long word form of this instruction is allowed.

Syntax: EXG Rx,Ry

Opcode: 1100xxx1dd00ayyy

x is the number of one register (the data register in a mixed exchange)

d is the type of exchange:

01 = exchange of same type of register, 10 = exchange between data and address register

a determines type of register:

0 = data register exchange, 1 = address register exchange (or mixed exchange)

y is the number of the other register (the address register in a mixed exchange)

Example: C38Ah = EXG D1,A2: swap the contents of D1 and A2

Flags: unchanged

EXT

An instruction that allows a two's complement value held in the low byte or word of a data register to be EXTended, so that the high bit is copied into each bit of the next byte or word.

Syntax: EXT Dn

Opcode: 010010001s000rrr

s is the size:

0 = extend byte to word, 1 = extend word to long word

r is the number of the data register

Example: 4880h = EXT.B D0: if D0 contained the value 0000000011111111 in its low word, this will be transformed to 1111111111111111

Flags: *N* and *F* react as normal

V and *C* are cleared

X is unaffected

ILLEGAL

This is the only instruction that is guaranteed to cause an ILLEGAL instruction trap on all processors in the 68000 family. Although many other bit patterns will cause this exception to occur on the 68008, Motorola reserves the right to use them for further enhancements to the instruction set.

Syntax: no assembler name

Opcode: 0100101011111100
Hex value: 4AFCh

Flags: unchanged

JMP

The PC is loaded with the effective address, causing a JuMP in program execution. The valid addressing modes are: (An), d(An), d(An,xi), Abs.W, Abs.L., d(PC), d(PC,xi).

Syntax: JMP <ea>

Opcode: 0100111011aaarrr
                  a is the effective addressing mode (see MOVE)
                  r is the effective addressing register (see MOVE)
Example: 4EF8h, 2000h = JMP 2000h (Abs.L): jump to the instruction at 2000h

Flags: unchanged

JSR

Jump to SubRoutine. As JMP, but prior to the loading of the PC, its old value (which is pointing to the next instruction), is pushed on to the stack. An RTS can then be used to return to the instruction following the JSR.

Syntax: JSR <ea>

Opcode: 0100111010aaarrr
                  a is the effective addressing mode (see MOVE)
                  r is the effective addressing register (see MOVE)
Example: 4E96h = JSR (A6): jump to the subroutine at the address pointed to by A6, saving the old PC value on the stack

Flags: unchanged

LEA

Load Effective Address is a way of loading an address register with the address of, rather than the value held by, the source. The addressing modes are the same as JMP, and the operation is long word in size, that is, it affects the whole register. In one of its simplest forms, such as LEA (A1),A2, all that occurs is that A2 is loaded with the value of A1: more useful are modes such as d(PC), which allow the programmer to calculate the actual value of the PC when writing position-independent code.

Syntax:	LEA <ea>,An
Opcode:	0100xxx111aaarrr
	x is the address register number
	a is the effective addressing mode (see MOVE)
	r is the effective addressing register (see MOVE)
Example:	41FAh, 0000h = LEA 0(PC),A0: this places the address of the source operand in A0; ie the value in the PC (which is pointing to the extension word) plus the displacement (0).
Flags:	unchanged

LINK

This is one of two instructions for sophisticated stack use. LINK performs a useful function by reserving stack space for use as local variables within a subroutine, which can then be accessed using the d(An) addressing mode. The first step is to save an address register on the stack which is then loaded with the value of the SP: this register now points to the first free space on the stack. To make room, a displacement (two's complement and therefore negative) is added to SP, leaving a gap in the stack that can be referenced using displacements added to the address register. The SP points to memory below the data area defined by the displacement, so further use of the stack is possible.

Syntax:	LINK An,#<disp>
Opcode:	0100111001010rrr + word containing displacement
	r is the number of the address register used as the pointer to the data area
Example:	4E56h, FFFAh = LINK A6,#−6: this saves the old value of A6 on the stack and points it to the next space down, and adds −6 to the SP, leaving six bytes free on the stack, accessible via A6
Flags:	unchanged

LSL

Logical Shift Left. Another of the shift/rotate group of instructions. The rules of ASL apply, and LSL is identical apart from its affect on the V flag, which is cleared.

Syntax: LSL Dx,Dy *or* LSL #<data>,Dy *or* LSL <ea>

Opcodes:
Memory: 1110001111aaarrr
Data register: 1110ccc1ssi01rrr
letters are as ASL

Flags: as ASL except V, which is always cleared

LSR

This is Logical Shift Right, similar to ASR with two exceptions: the highest bit of the operand is cleared (as opposed to being unaffected): so is the V flag.

Syntax: LSR Dx,Dy *or* LSR #<data>,Dy *or* LSR <ea>

Opcodes:
Memory: 1110001011aaarrr
Data register: 1110ccc0ssi01rrr
letters are as ASL

Flags: as ASR except *V*, which is cleared

MOVE

The most common instruction, MOVE, transfers data from a source to a destination.

Syntax: The assembler syntax is 'MOVE source to destination' — MOVE <ea>,<ea>.

The flexibility of the instruction is shown by the number of addressing modes that can be used. The source may be defined by any valid mode, so registers, external memory or immediate data can be used. The destination is slightly restricted. You cannot use an address register direct (but see MOVEA), PC relative addressing or immediate data. The size of the operation is defined as either byte, word or long word, affecting the low portion of the effective addresses in the case of byte or word. One important point which applies to using the address register direct is that you cannot use byte size; this applies to *all* direct address register references throughout the instruction set. The condition code flags are affected by MOVE, the final value of the destination determining their reaction.

Opcode: 00ssnnndddaaaarrr

The opcode for MOVE occupies at least one word of program space: up to four more words may be needed to define such things as absolute addresses or immediate data. The bit pattern above uses letters to define the variable bits in the instruction.

The size is controlled by bits 12 and 13, letter *s*. These can take one of three patterns:

01 means a byte size operation
11 means a word size operation
10 means a long word size operation

So, for example, an opcode with the high nibble 0011 will always be a word size MOVE operation. The remaining letters describe the source and destination. Six bits are needed to define an addressing mode; if a register is involved, then three of those bits will hold the number of the register, so a register number of 010 bin will mean register 2. The mode is also defined by three bits: the first seven values (000 to 110) describe effective addressing involving registers. If the mode is 111, then the register bits are used to further specify the addressing mode. The letters in MOVE have the following meaning:

s (already covered) is the size
n is the destination register number
d is the destination mode
a is the source mode
r is the source register number

Note that the mode and register bits are in a different order for destination and source, register/mode and mode/register respectively.

Addressing modes: The addressing modes are defined by the following bit patterns:

EFFECTIVE ADDRESSING		MODE (*a* and *d*)	REGISTER (*r* and *n*)
Dn	Data register direct	000	number
An	Address register direct	001	number
(An)	Address register indirect (ARI)	010	number
(An)+	ARI with post-increment	011	number
−(An)	ARI with predecrement	100	number

d(An)	ARI with displacement	101	number
d(An,ix)	ARI with displacement and index	110	number
Abs.W	Absolute word	111	000
Abs.L	Absolute long word	111	001
d(PC)	Program counter with displacement	111	010
d(PC,ix)	Program counter with displacement and index	111	011
Imm	Immediate data	111	100

The first column gives the standard assembler notation for each mode. *Note:* Many other instructions use the aaarrr format to define an effective address, in which case the above table can be used to calculate the effective addressing mode. For an example of calculating a MOVE opcode, let us use the instruction MOVE.B (A1),D2: move the byte of data at the address held in A1 into the low byte of D2. The high four bits are 0001; the destination register is 2 (010) and the destination mode data register direct (000). So far, the instruction word reads 0001010000aaarrr. The source mode is address register indirect (010) and the source register number 1 (001), so the final form is 0001010000010001 bin, or 1411h.

The effective address modes available on the 68008 are as follows:

Data register direct: The address referred to is the data register itself. If D6 is a destination, then it will receive the result of an operation. Notice that, in this case, the phrase 'address' does not mean an external memory location.

Address register direct: The specified address register is the effective address. If A5 is a source, then the value held in that address register is to be used. You may never use this mode for byte-sized operations.

Address register indirect: Here an address register holds the address of the data so, if A2 contained 2000h, then that is the address in external memory at which the operand resides (operand can mean destination or source). If the instruction requires a word or long word, then the most significant byte is at the address held in A2 and the remaining byte or bytes are in subsequent addresses. For example, if you MOVE.L FFAA6622h to (A2) then, with A2 containing 2000h, the byte FFh would be written to 2000h, AAh would go into 2001h, 66h into 2002h and 22h into 2003h.

Address register indirect with post-increment: This follows the same pattern as (An), with the extra bonus that the address register which supplies the operand address is incremented after being used. It can be thought of as two separate instructions, for instance MOVE.W D0, (A1)+ places the low word of D1 into the addresses (A1) and (A1)+1 and then adds 2 to A1 so that it points to the next word higher in memory. The increment automatically assumes the size of the instruction, so a byte-sized operation adds 1 to the address register, word size adds 2 and long word size adds 4.

Address register indirect with predecrement: Where (An)+ increments after referencing, −(An) subtracts the size of the instruction from the address register before using it as the operand address. The 68008 does not need push and pull instructions for stack operations, as MOVE <ea>,−(A7) places the source operand at the address pointed to by A7, the user stack pointer (or if in supervisor mode A7′, the SSP), and then points the SP to the next location downwards on the stack. Likewise, (A7)+ can pull data from the stack and restore the SP. Both modes are also useful for searching through or moving blocks of data.

Address register indirect with displacement: The address register has a displacement, contained in an extension word to the instruction, added to it before being used to reference the operand. The result of the addition is discarded, however, so as to leave the address register unaffected. If, for example, A1 is pointing to the start of a block of data and you wish to fetch the third byte of the block without altering A1, MOVE.B 3(A1),D1 will place the relevant byte into D1 without corrupting A1. The displacement value is a 16-bit two's complement number, so it is possible to refer to addresses 32K bytes either side of the pointer.

Address register indirect with displacement and index: This allows not only the addition of a two's complement 8-bit number (−128 to +127) but also a further indexed displacement taken from a register. The value may be the long integer contents or the two's complement low word contents; either data or address registers may supply the displacement. The extension word required for this addressing mode takes the form:

Extension: trrrs000dddddddd
              t is the type of register:
              if t=0 then a data register, if t=1 then an address register
              r is the number of the register
              s defines the size of the index
              if s=0 then index is two's complement 16-bit, if s=1 then
              index is integer 32-bit
              d is the fixed displacement

Absolute word: The address of the operand is supplied as an extension word. For example, MOVE.L 2000h,D0 will move the word held at addresses 2000h and 2001h into D0.

Absolute long: Two extension words provide the address.

Program counter with displacement: This allows reference to addresses relative to the current value of the PC, for the writing of position indepen-

dent code. As d(An), except that, instead of the address register supply-
ing the base address, the value of the PC (pointing to the extension word)
is used.

Program counter with displacement and index: The PC relative version of
d(An,ix). The same rules apply to the extension word.

Immediate data: The actual value is contained within extension words to
the instruction. If the instruction is byte-size, the low byte of one extension word is used; for a word-size, only one word needs to be supplied;
long word requires two extension words. The immediate mode cannot be
used to define a destination; it would be a very badly written program to
try to do so!

From the above information, you may well have spotted that some versions of MOVE could require up to four extension words: MOVE.L
#FFFFFFFF,200000h for example. There is a strict order for these
words, following the instruction proper. Any immediate data follows the
opcode, either one or two words. Next in line is the extension word
defining the source effective address; this could be an absolute long word,
word, displacement word or index and displacement word. Any words
required to define the destination bring up the rear. As immediate data
will be a source, the MOVE instruction can be up to five words long. The
above order applies to other instructions.

Flags: The normal reaction of the condition code flags is listed below,
along with their reaction to MOVE:

N is set if the MS bit of the result is 1, otherwise cleared.
Z is set if the result is zero, otherwise cleared.
Both *N* and *Z* react as normal to MOVE.
V is set if an arithmetic overflow occurs, otherwise cleared.
C is set if a carry occurs, otherwise cleared.
Both *V* and *C* are cleared by MOVE.
X, when affected, reacts as *C*.
MOVE leaves *X* unchanged.

MOVE to CCR

This is a special move instruction which places the low byte of the source
into the condition code register. However, this is actually a word-size
instruction that ignores the high byte supplied. Any addressing mode
except address register direct is allowed.

Syntax: MOVE <ea>,CCR

Opcode: 0100010011aaarrr
a is the effective address mode (see MOVE)
r is the effective address register (see MOVE)

Flags: *C, V, Z, N* and *X* are set to the value of bits 0 to 4 of the
source respectively

MOVE to SR

This is a move instruction that affects the whole status register. As you
might expect, it is word-sized. The source can use any effective address
(ea) except address register direct. This is a privileged instruction as it can
change the processor state: an attempt to use it in user mode will cause a
trap via vector 8. See AND to SR.

Syntax: MOVE <ea>,SR

Opcode: 0100011011aaarrr
a is the effective addressing mode (see MOVE)
r is the effective addressing register (see MOVE)

Flags: as MOVE to CCR

MOVE from SR

The status register is used as a source in this word-sized instruction. The
destination may *not* use addressing modes An, d(PC), d(PC,ix) or Imm.

Syntax: MOVE SR,<ea>

Opcode: 0100000011aaarrr
a is the effective addressing mode (see MOVE)
r is the effective addressing register (see MOVE)

Flags: unchanged

MOVE USP

A privileged instruction that accesses the User Stack Pointer (A7), when
the CPU is in supervisor state — and therefore the SSP (A7') is addressed
by references to A7. It can use the USP as either a source or destination;
the other operand is an address register. All of the registers are affected.

Syntax: MOVE USP,An *or* MOVE An,USP

Opcode: 010011100110dnnn
                     d is the direction of the move:
                     if d=0 then the USP is the destination, if d=1 then the
                     USP is the source
                     n is the number of the address register
Flags: unchanged

MOVEA

MOVE Address. As MOVE does not allow address register direct addressing for the destination, MOVEA is provided. Size is limited to word or long word: any mode may define the source. The flags are not affected by MOVEA, which is the main reason for the instruction being given a separate name (the bit pattern of the opcode fits that of MOVE). This is a deliberate ploy to aid programming.

Syntax: MOVEA <ea>,An
Opcode: 00ssnnn001aaarrr
                     s is the size (see ADD)
                     n is the destination register number
                     a is the source effective addressing mode (see MOVE)
                     r is the source effective addressing register (see MOVE)
Example: 307Ch,FFFFh = MOVEA.L #FFFFh,A0: load A0 with
                     the immediate data FFFFh
Flags: unchanged

MOVEM

The M suffix of this move instruction indicates Multiple registers. This is a kind of block instruction, where you provide a list of registers in the form of a 16-bit mask. Each bit relates to a register: if set, the register contents are either stored, or retrieved from external memory. The first location is defined by an effective address and subsequent addresses are either consecutively higher or lower. The size of the operation may be either word or long word, but in the case of word-size, the whole register is affected because the data is sign-extended to 32 bits (ie FFFFh becomes FFFFFFFFh). There are three types of MOVEM. Moving data from memory to registers allows all effective addressing modes except Dn, An, −(An) and Imm. Transferring from register to memory only allows (An),

−(An), d(An), d(An,xi), Abs.W and Abs.L; in this case −(An) is a special case which fetches data from consecutively lower addresses, whereas all other modes use increasing addresses. −(An) also uses a reversed bit mask to dictate the registers to be affected. Note that the −(An) mode is effectively a multiple stacking instruction (particularly using A7), with (An)+ the unstacking equivalent.

Syntax:	MOVEM <list>,<ea>
Opcode:	01001d001saaarrr + register mask
	d is the direction of the transfer:
	if d=0 then register to memory, if d=1 then memory to register
	s is the size:
	if s=0 then word, if s=1 then long word
	a is the effective addressing mode (see MOVE)
	r is the effective addressing register (see MOVE)
	The bits of the register mask normally relate to the following registers: bits 15 to 8 (A7 to A0 respectively); bits 7 to 0 (D7 to D0 respectively). In the −(An) mode the pattern is a complete mirror image.
Example:	48A7h,0007h = MOVEM.L D0–D2, −(A7). This places D0, D1 and D2 on the stack. (The register list uses a '−' to mean inclusive so D0–D2 means data registers 0, 1 and 2. A '/' separates non-consecutive registers.)
Flags:	unchanged

MOVEP

An instruction designed to help communication with hardware attached to the data bus. MOVE Peripheral data transfers byte values between data registers and alternative bytes of memory space (which may well have hardware peripherals located there). The operation is word or long-word-sized. The memory is pointed to using the d(An) addressing mode.

Syntax:	MOVEP Dx,d(Ay) *or* MOVEP d(Ay),Dx
Opcode:	0000nnn1ds001rrr + 16-bit displacement value
	n is the data register number
	d is the direction:
	if d=0 then memory to register, if d=1 then register to memory
	s is the size:
	if s=0 then word, if s=1 then long word

	r is the address register number
Example:	01C8h, 0000h = MOVEP.L D0,0(A0): if, for example, D0 contained FFAA6622h and A0 pointed to 2000h, after the operation 2000h would contain FFh, 2002h would contain AAh, 2004h 66h and 2006h 22h
Flags:	unchanged

MOVEQ

MOVE Quick, as its name implies, is a fast way of moving an 8-bit value into a data register. The value is sign-extended to 32 bits. The speed is achieved by the data being contained in the opcode itself.

Syntax:	MOVEQ #<data>,Dn
Opcode:	0111nnn0ddddddddd *n* is the data register number *d* is the data
Example:	700Fh = MOVEQ #0Fh,D0; loads D0 with 0000000Fh
Flags:	*N* and *Z* act as normal *V* and *C* are always cleared *X* is unchanged

MULS

Multiply Signed. Two 16-bit numbers are taken, one from an effective address (other than address register direct), the other from a data register, and multiplied together using signed arithmetic. The result is stored in the data register.

Syntax:	MULS <ea>,Dn
Opcode:	1100nnn111aaarrr *n* is the data register number *a* is the effective addressing mode (see MOVE) *r* is the effective register number (see MOVE)
Example:	C5C1h = MULS D1,D2: multiply, using signed arithmetic, the low order word contents of D1 and D2, placing the 32-bit result in D2
Flags:	*N* and *Z* act as normal *V* and *C* are always cleared *X* is unchanged

99

MULU

MULtiply Unsigned. As MULS but using unsigned arithmetic.

Syntax: MULU <ea>,Dn
Opcode: 1100nnn011aaarrr
             letters are as MULS
Flags: as MULS

NBCD

Negate BCD with extend. Negate means subtract from zero; the extend bit is included in the subtraction. This is a binary coded decimal operation. The only size allowed is byte, and all addressing modes except An, d(PC), d(PC,xi) and Imm may define the source.

Syntax: NBCD <ea>
Opcode: 0100100000aaarrr
             a is the effective addressing mode (see MOVE)
             r is the effective register number (see MOVE)
Flags: *N* and *V* are unpredictable
             Z is cleared if the result is not zero, else unchanged
             C and *X* react as normal

NEG

NEGate. Subtract the destination from zero. Any size may be used: the addressing modes are as NBCD.

Syntax: NEG <ea>
Opcode: 01000100ssaaarrr
             s is the size (see ADD)
             a is the effective addressing mode (see MOVE)
             r is the effective register number (see MOVE)
Example: 4400h = NEG.B D0: subtract the contents of the low byte of D0 from zero, placing the result back in the low byte of D0
Flags: *N*, *Z* and *V* react as normal
             C and *X* are cleared if the result is zero, else set

NEGX

As NEG, with the X flag included in the subtraction.

Syntax:	NEGX <ea>
Opcode:	01000000ssaaarrr
	letters are as NEG
Flags:	N, V, C and X as normal
	z is cleared if the result is not zero, else unchanged

NOP

This stands for No OPeration, and it does precisely that: surprisingly useful when writing and debugging programs.

Syntax:	NOP
Opcode:	0100111001110001
Hex value:	4E71h
Flags:	unchanged

NOT

A logical operation that complements the individual bits of the destination. All addressing modes except An, d(PC), d(PC,xi) and Imm are valid: any size may be used.

Syntax:	NOT <ea>
Opcode:	01000110ssaaarrr
	s is the size (see ADD)
	a is the effective addressing mode (see MOVE)
	r is the effective addressing register (see MOVE)
Flags:	N and Z react as normal
	V and C always cleared
	X unaffected

OR

Using the logical OR rule, the bits of the source and destination are processed and the result placed in the destination. One of the operands must be a data register: if this is the destination, then the source may use any addressing mode bar An; if the data register is a source, then modes Dn, An, d(PC), d(PC,xi) or Imm cannot specify the destination. This instruction can use any size.

Syntax: OR <ea>,Dn *or* OR Dn,<ea>

Opcode: 10000nnndssaaarrr
           n is the data register number
           d is the direction:
           if d=0 then data register is destination, if d=1 then data register is source
           s is the size (see ADD)
           a is the effective addressing mode (see MOVE)
           r is the effective addressing register (see MOVE)

Flags: *N* and *Z* act as normal
           V and *C* are cleared
           X is unchanged

ORI

The Immediate version of OR: see ANDI.

Syntax: ORI #<data>,<ea>

Opcode: 00000000ssaaarrr + one or two words
           s is the size (see ADD)
           a is the effective addressing mode (see MOVE)
           r is the effective addressing register (see MOVE)

Flags: as ANDI

ORI to CCR

An OR version of ANDI to CCR.

Syntax: ORI #xxx,CCR

Opcode: 0000000000111100 + word
Hex value: 003Ch

Flags: as ANDI to CCR

ORI to SR

An OR version of ANDI to SR.

Syntax:	ORI #xxx,SR
Opcode:	0000000001111100 + word
Hex value:	007Ch
Flags:	as ANDI to SR

PEA

Push Effective Address. The actual address specified by the addressing mode is placed on the stack by this long-sized operation. Valid modes are: (An), d(An), d(An,xi), Abs.W., Abs.L., d(PC) and d(PC,xi).

Syntax:	PEA <ea>
Opcode:	0100100001aaarrr
	a is the effective addressing mode (see MOVE)
	r is the effective addressing register (see MOVE)
Example:	4853h = PEA A3: if A3 pointed to 2000h, this value would be pushed as a long word, on to the stack
Flags:	unchanged

RESET

If in user mode, a trap through vector 8 will occur, as this is a privileged instruction. If in supervisor mode, the reset control pin is asserted to reset external devices. This instruction takes 136 clock cycles to execute, providing time for the devices to respond.

Syntax:	RESET
Opcode:	0100111001110000
Hex value:	4E70h
Flags:	unchanged

ROL

A rotate instruction: ROL means ROtate Left. This consists of shifting left the operand (see ASL), but, as well as the MS bit being placed in the carry, it is also copied into the LS bit, giving a circular effect. In fact, ROL a byte eight times and it will return to its original value. The various methods of applying ROL are the same as ASL.

Syntax: ROL Dx,Dy (Dx specifies number of rotates)
ROL #<data>,Dy (data specifies number of rotates)
ROL <ea>, (one rotate only, word size)

Opcodes:
Memory: 1110011111aaarrr
Data register: 1110ccc1ssi11rrr
letters are as ASL

Flags: N and Z react as normal
C set as last bit copied into it
V cleared
X unchanged

ROR

ROtate Right: the bits are shifted in the opposite direction to ROL, the LS bit being copied into the carry and MS bit. The rules of ASL apply.

Syntax: see ROL
Opcodes:
Memory: 1110011011aaarrr
Data register: 1110ccc0ssi11rrr
letters are as ASL
Flags: as ROL

ROXL

ROtate X Left. An instruction that includes the extend flag in the rotation. The MS bit is copied into both C and X: the old value of X is transferred to the LS bit of the operand. Therefore ROXL applied to a byte is in effect a 9-bit rotate. Otherwise as ASL and ROL.

Syntax: see ROL
Opcodes:
Memory: 1110010111aaarrr
Data register: 1110ccc1ssi10rrr
letters are as ASL

Flags: *N* and *Z* as normal
                  V always cleared
                  X set as last bit copied into it. Unaffected for zero count
                  C as *X*, except it takes value of X fopr a zero count

ROXR

The Righthand version of ROXL.

Syntax: see ROL
Opcodes:
Memory: 1110010011aaarrr
Data register: 1110ccc0ssi10rrr
                   letters are as ASL
Flags: as ROXL

RTE

ReTurn from Exception. This is a privileged instruction used to return to a program after exception processing has been completed following a trap. Return from exception pulls the previous contents of the SR and PC from the stack and restores them, so that the old program continues.

Syntax: RTE
Opcode: 0100111001110011
Hex value: 4E73h
Flags: old values retrieved from stack

RTR

ReTurn and Restore condition codes. This allows the retrieval of the CC flags and PC from the stack.

Syntax: RTR
Opcode: 0100111001110111
Hex value: 4E77h
Flags: old values retrieved from stack

RTS

This is the normal way of returning from a subroutine. See BSR and JSR. The PC is loaded with the value pointed to by A7 (A7' if in supervisor mode) after it has been incremented.

Syntax:	RTS
Opcode:	0100111001110101
Hex value:	4E75h
Flags:	unchanged

SBCD

Subtract BCD. Refer to ABCD, as this is the subtract version and all the same rules apply.

Syntax:	SBCD Dy,Dx *or* SBCD −'(Ay),−(Ax)
Opcode:	1000xxx10000myyy the letters are as ABCD
Flags:	as ABCD

Scc

Set according to condition code: this allows, amongst other things, the making of a more permanent record of the state of the flags. It will test for the specified condition, as does Bcc, and set the destination byte to FFh if the condition is met, otherwise clear the byte. The destination can be specified by all addressing modes except An, d(PC), d(PC,xi) and Imm. Note that using the TRUE condition is a quick way of setting a byte to FFh.

Syntax:	Scc <ea>
Opcode:	0101cccc11aaarrr c is the condition (see Bcc and DBcc) a is the effective addressing mode (see MOVE) r is the effective register (see MOVE)
Example:	57C0h = SEQ D0: if the zero flag is set, load the low byte of D0 with FFh, otherwise 00h
Flags:	unchanged

STOP

This is a privileged instruction which causes the CPU to 'hang up' until a valid interrupt or a reset signal is received. It is accompanied by a word of immediate data which is loaded into the SR before the STOP. A Trace will occur if the old T bit is set, and a privilege violation exception will begin if you try to load the S bit with 0.

Syntax:	STOP #xxx
Opcode:	0100111001110010 + word
Hex value:	4E72h
Flags:	set as bits 5 to 0 of the immediate data

SUB

This is the SUBtract instruction. As with ADD, a data register must be one of the operands; the source is subtracted from the destination and the result stored in the destination. The other rules of ADD apply.

Syntax:	SUB <ea>,Dn *or* SUB Dn,<ea>
Opcode:	1001nnnmssaaarrr the letters are as ADD
Flags:	all react as normal

SUBA

The subtract version of ADDA.

Syntax:	SUBA <ea>,An
Opcode:	1001nnns11aaarrr the letters are as ADDA
Flags:	not affected

SUBI

The subtract version of ADDI

Syntax:	SUBI #data,<ea>
Opcode:	00000100ssaaarrr + one or two words the letters are as SUBI
Flags:	all react as normal

SUBQ

SUBtract Quick: see ADDQ.

Syntax:	SUBQ #<data>,<ea>
Opcode:	0101ddd1ssaaarrr the letters are as ADDQ
Flags:	all react as normal

SUBX

SUBtract with eXtend: the extend bit is subtracted along with the source from the destination. See ADDX for the rules.

Syntax:	SUBX Dy,Dx *for* SUBX $-(Ay),-(Ax)$
Opcode:	1001xxx1ss00myyy the letters are as SUBX
Flags:	all react as normal

SWAP

This instruction applies to a data register: it swaps bits 0 to 15 with bits 16 to 31, allowing access to the top half for instructions unable to reach it.

Syntax:	SWAP Dn
Opcode:	0100100001000rrr *r* is the data register number
Example:	4840h = SWAP D0: if D0 contained FFFF0000h, after the instruction it will contain 0000FFFFh
Flags:	*N* is set if bit 31 of the result is set, else cleared *Z* is set if the result is zero, else cleared *V* and *C* are always cleared *X* is unaffected

TAS

Test And Set a destination. The destination may be a byte referred to by any of the addressing modes except An, d(PC), d(PC,xi) and Imm. The N and Z flags react to the byte and then bit 7 of the destination is set.

Syntax: TAS <ea>

Opcode: 0100101011aaarrr
         a is the effective addressing mode (see MOVE)
         r is the effective register (see MOVE)

Flags: *N* and *Z* react as normal
         V and *C* are cleared
         X is unchanged

TRAP

A method of forcing exception processing through software. The TRAP vectors may be used for important system calls. A four-bit number contained with the instruction determines which vector (number + 32) is used.

Syntax: TRAP #<vector>

Opcode: 010011100100vvvv
         v is the vector number (0 to 15)

Flags: unchanged

TRAPV

A special, conditional TRAP instruction that only causes an exception if the V (overflow) flag is set. If a trap occurs it uses vector 7.

Syntax: TRAPV

Opcode: 0100111001110110
Hex value: 4E76h

Flags: unchanged

TST

The byte, word or long word of the destination is TeSTed and the flags set as appropriate. The destination may be defined with all addressing modes except An, d(PC), d(PC,xi) and Imm.

Syntax: TST <ea>

Opcode: 01001010ssaaarrr
         s is the size (see ADD)

                       a is the effective addressing mode (see MOVE)
                       r is the effective register (see MOVE)

Flags: set according to the destination tested

UNLK

UNLinK reverses the process performed by LINK. The SP is loaded from the specified address register, which is then loaded with the value unstacked from the new top of the stack.

Syntax: UNLK An
Opcode: 0100111001011rrr
                 r is the address register number
Flags: unaffected

CHAPTER 8
Exploring Machine Code

The previous two chapters have described the 68008 microprocessor. The time has now come to demonstrate some simple routines. Program 8.1 is a short SuperBASIC program which installs a simple machine code routine in the QL's memory and then passes control to the code. Before we run through the features of the program, enter the SuperBASIC: you may omit the REMark statements if you wish. Having entered the program, SAVE it before running, as any errors in the DATA statements will almost certainly lead to a 'crash' — to recover a crashed program when running machine code, you will probably have to press the reset button and therefore destroy the memory's contents.

Program 8.1: Machine Code Demo

```
100 REMark machine code demo
110 REMark
120  CLEAR
130 REMark
140 REMark Reserve space for code
150 REMark
160  start=RESPR(32)
170 REMark
180 REMark Start now points to space.
190 REMark Poke code into space.
200 REMark
210  FOR location=start TO start + 20 STEP 2
220    READ word
230    POKE_W location,word
240  END FOR location
250 REMark
260 REMark Prepare to run code.
270 REMark
280  CLS
290  PRINT "press a function key"
300  REPeat wait: IF KEYROW(0) THEN EXIT wait
310 REMark
320 REMark Run the code.
330 REMark
340  CALL start
350 REMark
360 REMark Return from code routine.
370 REMark
```

```
380   AT 12,12:PRINT "Code has run."
390   STOP
400  REMark
410  REMark Machine code as data.
420  REMark
430   DATA 8316,2,0
440  REMark MOVEA.L #20000,A0
450   DATA 8252,0,8192
460  REMark MOVE.L #2000,D0
470   DATA 17048
480  REMark CLR.L (A0)+
490   DATA 20936,65532
500  REMark DBRA D0,-4
510   DATA 28672
520  REMark MOVEQ #0,D0
530   DATA 20085
540  REMark RTS
```

When safely stored on microdrive, try out the program. When it runs, a message asking you to press a function key will appear. After your response, the machine code will be called from SuperBASIC, and it is at this point that a crash is most likely. If all is well, the whole screen will be cleared to black and a message announcing success will be displayed. You may not be too impressed with the result — the machine code needs to fill with zero each memory location which stores the screen display in order to achieve this effect.

To put things into perspective, try the following single line of Super-BASIC: For x=131072 TO 163836 STEP 4: POKE_L x,0. The effect is the same, but you will agree that it is somewhat slower!

The first stage of the program is the RESPR keyword: this reserves space at the top of memory. RESPR stands for RESident PRocedure. The number of bytes set aside is dictated by the value in brackets following the keyword. Not only is RESPR a command, (it frees an area of memory from the danger of being used by SuperBASIC or QDOS), but it is also a function (it returns a value, the address of the first free memory location). By using the statement 'start=RESPR (32)', we make the variable 'start' equal to the first free address of a newly created space of 32 bytes of memory.

The next step is to transfer the machine code into this space. This is done by storing the code in DATA statements, a word at a time, in their decimal form. The words are POKEd into place by a FOR loop, creating a machine code routine that exists in RAM. Note that, although we have used decimal for convenience, the opcodes are stored in memory as binary numbers. For example, if you use the byte version of POKE to place, say, 170 dec into one byte of memory, the eight bits of that location will take up the binary pattern 10101010. All 68008 machine code instructions are a minimum of one word long, so each instruction is POKEd in with the POKE_W command.

With the code in place, the program now invites you to execute it, using the short form of REPEAT to test whether you have pressed a function key. The routine is then executed with the CALL command, and on return to SuperBASIC a suitable message is displayed.

As CALL is not fully explained, at least in early QL manuals, a description of the command is worthwhile. One parameter is essential: the starting address of the machine code routine. CALL 0 will transfer the processor to interpret the values stored at address 0, despite the fact that they do not constitute a valid program and will cause the computer to lock up. This is the first important point about CALL. All other SuperBASIC functions and commands (should) give error messages when used improperly. Up to 13 further parameters can be supplied; these are placed in data registers D1 to D7 and address registers A0 to A5 respectively. Therefore 'CALL start,20,40,60' will place 20 into D1, 40 into D2 and 60 to D3: you cannot load a value into D4 without also specifying values for D1, D2 and D3. The machine code routine must not use A6 and A7 without restoring their original values before using the RTS (return from subroutine) instruction. However, register D0 is used by Super-BASIC to indicate an error condition. It is loaded with −15 (two's complement style) before the program counter is loaded with the CALL address, so if you leave D0 unchanged and return to SuperBASIC, the program will halt with error message 15, 'bad parameter'. If you load D0 with zero, then SuperBASIC continues as normal after the call: if a positive value is placed into D0, then you can create your own error messages. How this can be done will be demonstrated later in the chapter.

So much for the SuperBASIC — how does the code work? The remarks in Program 8.1 following each DATA statement give the instructions represented by the decimal values. The CALL instruction, after loading the registers as required, performs a JSR (jump to subroutine) instruction, placing the old contents of the PC on the user stack and reloading the PC with the CALL address. Therefore, the next instruction that the CPU fetches is from address 'start'.

The code fetched for decoding by the 68008 is 8316 dec or 2076Ch (line 430): if you translate this into binary (0010000000111100) and refer to the MOVEA instruction in the previous chapter, you will see that it is a long form of the MOVEA code. The destination is register A0 and the source is immediate data. This data is contained in the next two words of memory (long data being required) so the processor dutifully fetches them, updating the PC as it goes, and places the long word data 20000h into A0.

The first instruction being completed, the next is fetched and acted upon. This, 8252 dec or 203Ch (line 450), translates as MOVE.L #2000h,D0. The 2000h is immediate data again, contained in the next two words of program. So now we have A0 containing 20000h, which happens to be the start of the screen area, and D0 containing 2000h, which is the size, in words, of that area.

The next instruction is 17048 dec, or 4298h. This is CLR.L (A0)+. The CPU places a long word zero (four bytes or 32 bits) into the memory locations pointed to by A0, so that locations 20000h to 20003h are set to zero: the CPU then adds 4 to A0 so that it points to the next long word. In effect, the first small section of the screen has been 'blacked out': an explanation of why this occurs will be given in Chapter 10, on the screen display.

We have cleared the first part of the screen, and now the routine employs a condition looping instruction to continue the operation. 20936 dec, or 51C8h is the first word of a DBcc instruction. The type used is DBF, or decrement and branch if false: this can be written as DBRA (decrement and branch always) as the false condition means that the condition test is always met. If you study DBcc you will see that it uses a data register as a counter, and in this case D0 is specified. The data register has 1 subtracted from it, and if the result is −1 then no further action is taken — the CPU passes on to the next instruction. However, the first time this instruction is encountered, D0 contains 2000h, and the branch is therefore performed. The second word of the instruction, 65532 dec, is added to the PC but, because the instruction uses a sign extended form of arithmetic, 65532 decimal becomes FFFFFFFCh; adding this 32-bit number to the 32-bit PC has the effect of subtracting 4 from the PC. Four bytes earlier than the last value of the PC, the processor encounters the CLR instruction.

This time round, A0 is pointing to the next screen long word, which is cleared as before, and the CPU finds itself processing the DBRA instruction again. D0 minus one is still only 1FFEh, so the whole procedure is repeated. Each time round, D0 is decremented, until, many times round the loop later, it finally reaches −1 and the branch does not occur. By that time, the whole of the screen area has been cleared.

Having escaped from the loop, the processor fetches the value 28672 or 7000h. This is MOVEQ #0,D0, and serves to set up the data register so that no error message will result on return to SuperBASIC. The final code, 20085 dec or 4E75h, is RTS. The old value of the PC is pulled from the stack and restored to the PC; control reverts to the program which called our machine code subroutine, and the computer is back to running its SuperBASIC interpreter program.

The above example is very simple. You may like to try altering the immediate values in the machine code so that only a part of the screen is cleared, or perhaps instead of the CLR instruction you could MOVE a value on to the screen other than zero (take care that you increase the branch offset when placing a longer instruction within the DBRA loop).

(Add to Program 8.1)

Program 8.2: Custom Error Messages

```
400 REMark Custom error messages.
410 REMark Machine code as data.
420 REMark
430  DATA 16890,6
440 REMark LEA 6(PC),A0
450  DATA 8200
460 REMark MOVE.L A0,D0
470  DATA 20085
480 REMark RTS
490  DATA 12
500 REMark Length of message
510  DATA 18533,27756,28448
520  DATA 29800,25970,25889
530 REMark Message data
```

I mentioned earlier that your own custom error messages could be generated on return to SuperBASIC from machine code. This is achieved by
loading D0 with the address of an area of memory which contains the
required message. The first word contains a value that represents the
number of characters in the message, and subsequent bytes contain the
message coded in ASCII. To demonstrate this, delete the DATA statements from the first program and add the new ones shown as Program 8.2.
Run the program as before. Instead of the 'Code has run' message, the
SuperBASIC halts with the string which is embedded in the machine code.
If you want to alter the message, the ASCII codes are given in the 'character
set' section of the QL manual. If you examine the code you will notice that
it uses program counter relative addressing; this allows the routine to be
position-independent.

Program 8.3: Monitor

```
100 REMark _____ Monitor_____
110 set_up
120 REPeat menu
130  screen
140  getfun
150  SELect ON req
160   ON req=2
170   F_1
180   ON req=8
190   F_2
200   ON req=16
210   F_3
220   ON req=1
230   F_4
240   ON req=32
250   F_5
```

Inside the Sinclair QL

```
260   END SELect
270  END REPeat menu
280  REMark _____
290  DEFine PROCedure set_up
300   MODE 8
310   OPEN #3,scr_448x24a32x0
320   BORDER #3,2,7
330   CSIZE #3,3,1
340   WINDOW 448,192,32,24
350  END DEFine set_up
360  REMark _____
370  DEFine PROCedure screen
380   CLS:CLS #0:CLS #3
390   PRINT #3,,"Monitor Menu"
400   RESTORE
410   AT 3,0
420   FOR text= 1 TO 5
430    READ a$
440    PRINT"   Function ";text;":-",a$;"."\\\
450   END FOR text
460   FLASH #0,1
470   PRINT #0,,"Press a function key"
480   FLASH #0,0
490   DATA "Examine Memory","Change memory"
495   DATA "Run machine code","Convert numbers"
497   DATA "Save code"
500  END DEFine screen
510  REMark _____
520  DEFine PROCedure F_1
530   CLS #0:CLS
540   PRINT#3;"Address    Contents    ASCII"
550   REPeat new_add
560    prompt$="Starting Address"
570    get_num
580    num=2*INT(num/2)
590    options
600    REPeat display
610     FOR p=num TO num+24 STEP 2
620      SCROLL -10
630      print_line
640     END FOR p
650     num=p+2
660     getfun
670     IF req<>2 THEN EXIT display
680    END REPeat display
690    IF req<>8 THEN EXIT new_add
700   END REPeat new_add
710  END DEFine
720  REMark _____
730  DEFine PROCedure F_2
740  CLS
750  PRINT #3,,"Alter Memory"
760  REPeat start
770   prompt$="Change?"
780   get num
790   p=INT(num/2)*2
800   REPeat more
810    REPeat alter
```

116

```
820     print_line
830     prompt$="New value? (ENTER to exit)"
840     get_num
850     IF fetch$="" THEN EXIT alter
860     POKE_W p,num
870     print_line
880     SCROLL -10
890     p=p+2
900   END REPeat alter
910   options
920   getfun
930   IF req<>2 THEN EXIT more
940   p=p+2
950   SCROLL -10
960  END REPeat more
970  IF req<>8 THEN EXIT start
980 END REPeat start
990 END DEFine F_2
1000 REMark ------------------------------
1010 DEFine PROCedure F_3
1020   CLS:PRINT #3,,"To run code"
1030   REPeat newad
1040    prompt$="From where?"
1050    get_num
1060    num=2*INT(num/2)
1070    REPeat more
1080      CLS #0:CLS:AT 8,8
1090      PRINT"Code to run from"! hex$(num)\\,"F1 to run"
1100      getfun:CLS
1110      IF req=2 THEN
1120       CALL num
1130       AT 8,10
1140       PRINT "Code has run"
1150      END IF
1160      REPeat wait:IF NOT KEYROW(0) THEN EXIT wait
1170      options:getfun:CLS
1180      IF req<>2 THEN EXIT more
1190    END REPeat more
1200    IF req<>8 THEN EXIT newad
1210   END REPeat newad
1220 END DEFine F_3
1230 REMark ------------------------------
1240 DEFine PROCedure F_4
1250   CLS:PRINT #3,,"Conversion"
1260   REPeat BASE
1270    CLS #0
1280    PRINT #0,"F1- Hex > dec F2";"- Dec > hex F3- Menu"
1290    getfun
1300    IF req>8 THEN EXIT BASE
1310    IF req=2 THEN
1320     REPeat convhex
1330      prompt$="Hex value? (zero to exit)"
1340      get_num
1350      IF NOT num THEN EXIT convhex
1360      SCROLL -10
1370      AT 18,6
1380      PRINT"Hex"!hex$(num),"="!num!"Dec"
1390     END REPeat convhex
```

```
1400    ELSE
1410     REPeat convdec
1420      CLS #0
1430      INPUT#0,,"Dec value? (zero to exit)"\,num
1440      IF NOT num THEN EXIT convdec
1450      SCROLL -10
1460      AT 18,6
1470      PRINT "Dec"!num,"="!hex$(num)!"Hex"
1480     END REPeat convdec
1490     END IF
1500    END REPeat BASE
1510 END DEFine F_4
1520 REMark ------------------------------
1530 DEFine PROCedure F_5
1540   CLS:PRINT #3,"To save code"
1550   prompt$="First address?"
1560   get_num
1570   st=num
1580   prompt$="Last address?"
1590   get_num
1600   la=num-st
1610   CLS #0:INPUT #0\,"Name ?"!na$
1620   SBYTES ("mdv2_"&na$),st,la
1630 END DEFine F_5
1640 REMark ------------------------------
1650 DEFine PROCedure get_num
1660   REPeat fetch
1670    CLS #0
1680    POKE 163976,255
1690    INPUT #0,,(prompt$)\,fetch$
1700     num=dec(fetch$)
1710     IF num>-1 THEN EXIT fetch
1720      prompt$="Try again"
1730    END REPeat fetch
1740 END DEFine get_num
1750 REMark ------------------------------
1760 DEFine PROCedure getfun
1770   REPeat scan
1780    req=KEYROW(0)
1790     IF req AND req <>4 AND req<33 THEN EXIT scan
1800   END REPeat scan
1810   END DEFine getfun
1820 REMark ------------------------------
1830 DEFine PROCedure print_line
1840   LOCal a$
1850   AT 18,3
1860   a$="0000"&hex$(p)
1870   PRINT a$(LEN(a$)-4 TO LEN(a$)),
1880   a$="000"&hex$(ABS(PEEK_W(p)))
1890   PRINT a$(LEN(a$)-3 TO LEN(a$))
1900   AT 18,30
1910   PRINT asc$(PEEK(p))!!asc$(PEEK(p+1))
1920 END DEFine print_line
1930 REMark ------------------------------
1940 DEFine PROCedure options
1950   CLS #0:PRINT #0;"F1 - More ";
1955   PRINT "F2 - New Address F3 - Menu"
1960 END DEFine options
```

```
1970 REMark _____
1980 DEFine FuNction dec(a$)
1990  LOCal total,power,a%
2000  power=1
2010  total=0
2020  FOR place=LEN(a$) TO 1 STEP -1
2030    a%=(CODE(a$(place)))-48
2040    IF a%<0 OR a%>22 OR (a%>9 AND a%<17) THEN RETurn -1
2050    a%=a%-7*(a%>16)
2060    total=total+a%*power
2070    power=power*16
2080  END FOR place
2090  RETurn total
2100 END DEFine dec
2110 REMark --------------------------------
2120 DEFine FuNction hex$(a)
2130  LOCal h$,t,v
2140  h$="":v=a
2150  REPeat place
2160    t=v-INT(v/16)*16
2170    h$=CHR$(t+48+7*(t>9))&h$
2180    v=INT(v/16)
2190    IF NOT v THEN EXIT place
2200  END REPeat place
2210  RETurn h$
2220  END DEFine hex$
2230 REMark _____
2240 DEFine FuNction asc$(a%)
2250  a%=a% MOD 128
2260  IF a%<32 THEN RETurn "."
2270  RETurn CHR$(a%)
2280 END DEFine add$
```

This program is designed to allow simple experiments with machine code.
It will also be useful for running some of the hardware demonstrations in
later chapters. Program 8.3 is a menu-driven monitor program: it works
in hexadecimal numbers, but one option will convert numbers to and
from decimal. Being menu-driven, the program is straightforward to use.
Enter the program with care and save it a couple of times before trying it
out. When you run the program you will be presented with five options.
These operate as follows:

1) *Examine memory:* You are prompted for a starting address (in
   hexadecimal) and then memory locations are displayed a word at a
   time. The characters relating to the ASCII values of the contents are
   also displayed. After a block has been printed out, you have the option
   of continuing, entering a new address, or returning to the menu.
2) *Change memory:* This mode allows you to alter the contents of RAM
   and write to the I/O locations.
3) *Save code:* A useful function which allows code to be saved on micro-

drive before being run. It will prevent the need for much re-entering of data if a routine should crash.

4) *Convert numbers:* Performs hex to dec and dec to hex conversions.
5) *Run code:* Clears the screen and tests any routine you like.

I hope that the Monitor program will encourage you to experiment with 68008 machine code. Manual assembly of large routines can be rather tiresome, and in this case the purchase of a good assembler program will be money well spent. However, trying out a few simple routines will give you a great insight into how things work. The monitor will also be of use for exploring the memory map of the QL, the subject of the next chapter.

CHAPTER 9
The Memory Map

The basic QL computer comes complete with 128K of random access memory, in the form of 16 64K bit dynamic RAM chips (see Chapter 5). This is a generous allocation in comparison with eight-bit computers, but it is normal for the sort of serious applications for which the QL is intended. Expanding the amount of memory is possible: Sinclair themselves announced a 512K byte RAM board at the time of the QL's launch. With 20 address lines, the 68008 CPU is capable of directly addressing one megabyte of memory, although the QL reserves some of those locations for purposes other than program and data storage. In this chapter, we will look at the allocation of the memory addresses.

Figure 9.1 represents the memory map of the QL. Note that the drawing is not to scale. The first point to recognise is that there are 'holes' in the map, either where no circuitry will react at all, or where the simple decoding produces a spurious result. Without additional hardware, addresses above 3FFFFh are decoded as if the QL only possessed an 18-bit address bus; the effect of this is to create three 'reflections' of the low quarter of the map in the top threequarters. For example, try the Super-BASIC line PRINT PEEK_L (0), and compare the result when you replace the zero with 262144 (40000h), 524288 (80000h) and 786432 (C0000h). If you have no expansion hardware installed, the results will all be the same — the high two bits of the address bus are ignored.

Physical memory map

At the bottom is the system's built-in ROM containing the 'firmware' — the QDOS routines and SuperBASIC interpreter. Any attempt to write to these locations will be a lost cause. The ROMs occupy 48K of memory space, from 0 to 0BFFFh. If you use the monitor program to examine the first few locations of the ROM, you will discover the vector address discussed in Chapter 6. The first vector, at addresses 0 to 3, contains the long word first loaded into the SSP after switch-on or a reset. My QL (and most likely yours, unless major software changes are made to future machines) holds the address 30000h. The next vector, at addresses 4 to 7, contains 14Eh, the address loaded into the PC: this address is where we will find

HEXADECIMAL ADDRESSES	PHYSICAL MEMORY MAP	SOFTWARE MEMORY MAP	
FFFFF	INTERRUPT VECTORS		
FFFF3	EXPANSION RAM SPACE		
3FFFF	RANDOM ACCESS MEMORY	RAMT-1	RESIDENT PROCEDURES
		RESPR	TRANSIENT PROGRAMS
		TRNSP	
			SUPERBASIC PROGRAMS
		BASIC	
			FREE SPACE USED FOR FILE SLAVE BLOCKS
		FREE	
30000			HEAP AREA
	OPTIONAL SECOND SCREEN AREA	HEAP	
			SYSTEM TABLES AND SYSTEM VARIABLES
28000		BASE	
	SCREEN RAM AREA		
20000			
	INPUT/OUTPUT EXPANSION		
1C000			
	INPUT/OUTPUT HARDWARE		
18000			
	INPUT/OUTPUT EXPANSION		
10000			
	PLUG-IN ROM		
0C000			
	SYSTEM READ ONLY MEMORY		
00000			

Figure 9.1: QL Memory Map

the 'setting up' routine which organises the computer. It is important that these vectors are in ROM, because they must never disappear!

The next section of the map, from C000h to FFFFh, is a 16K space that is reserved for additional ROM software. The socket marked ROM at the back of the QL (which housed the overflow EPROM on early QLs) supplies a feed of the low 16 address lines to any cartridge plugged in, along with power, data and enable lines. After the initial 'bootstrapping' procedure which the QL follows after a reset, testing the RAM and installing the system variables, the first address of the plug-in ROM space is tested. If it contains a particular code, then a machine code call is made to the next location (C002h): this effectively passes over control to the software in the plug-in ROM, which may then run its own program or install extra commands into the computer; these can then be used to call up the extra ROM from SuperBASIC. Incidentally, the code that forces QDOS to call the ROM is 4AFBh. This is an illegal instruction which

Motorola reserve for their own products, unlike 4AFCh, the 'user' illegal code.

Further on up the map we encounter a 32K space reserved for expansion input and output devices: it is intended to allow the addition of further hardware. Without further additions to the QL, this area of memory will return spurious results.

Memory addresses 18000h to 1BFFFh host the hardware devices that are contained within the standard QL. Although these are not memory devices, they are addressed in a similar manner. The devices that respond to these addresses are termed I/O (input and output) devices. By writing to 18063h, for example, the CPU can send information to the 'master chip' (MC — the ZX8302), which controls the screen display. However, reading from 18063h will not affect the MC, as the read/write line of the CPU is also used in the decoding process. It is the correct combination of address and control lines that activates or elicits the response. Perhaps the simplest example of an I/O address is 18000h. Try the following single line of BASIC:

REPeat loop: AT 10,10: PRINT PEEK (98307); "–"

The result, as you will probably guess, is the output from the real-time clock: we are actually looking at the last byte, 18003h. By peeking the correct location, we are following the same procedure as the DATE command. It is possible to write to the clock as well, so as to adjust the date.

More space is allocated for expansion I/O from 1C000h to 1FFFFh.

The next address is 20000h, and this is the start of RAM in the memory map. The area up to 3FFFFh is occupied by the on-board memory chips, giving a space of 20000h, or 128K bytes. The first chunk, a 32K block extending to 27FFFh, is normally used for the screen display memory map. (This bit-mapped screen area is discussed further in Chapter 10.) I say 'normally', because there are provisions in the hardware to use a different area, although this involves moving the system variables. Certainly, a machine code program that bypassed the operating system could use two screen areas but, at the time of writing, it is not clear if this is possible to achieve from QDOS. I will therefore restrict further descriptions to the normal set-up.

Software memory map

Immediately after the screen area, a small block of RAM is used for system variables. The first 100h bytes store information for QDOS: pointers to the various tables, base values of the other memory areas and similar essential data. Following these QDOS variables are two tables that keep track of the filing systems. The QL uses a sophisticated method of creating and using files, so that, for example, a microdrive file has its own 'physical description', a routine that deals with the fact that the file is actually stored on a microdrive. The main section of the operating system need not be concerned with which type of 'physical' file it is dealing with. The next space up the map is occupied by the system stack, the area of memory pointed to by the SSP. This is only used when the CPU is in supervisor mode. The stack is only of a limited size: if too many values are pushed on to it, it will grow down into the system tables. There are 192 long word spaces available, but by the time a user attempts to operate the processor in supervisor mode, many of these have been occupied. It is recommended that only 64 bytes are used, and of course the SSP must be restored to its original value before performing an RTE to return to user mode.

Above the system stack, the areas of RAM are divided into two parts. At the bottom is the 'heap' — this is quite an apt title. It consists of a heap of tables used both by QDOS and any resident programs, and other assorted blocks of data. The heap is a somewhat disorganised stack, with the 68008's advanced addressing mode allowing access to the data despite the fact that it may move around in memory. This heap area grows upwards as more items are placed on to it.

Conversely, the other area of data grows downwards. This consists of three parts. At the top will be any space reserved by the RESPR function mentioned earlier — this is not unreasonably called the resident procedure area. Next down comes the transient program area, where machine code programs can be loaded. These must be self-contained, position-independent programs, as their location may alter depending on the state of the resident procedure area. Programs here can be run from SuperBASIC with the EXEC command, or QDOS can deal with them, so that a degree of concurrency is possible. Finally, the section that you may have thought I was never going to mention — SuperBASIC! Any programs and data loaded into the QL will be placed below the transient program area (which, along with the resident procedure area, may not exist). The larger the SuperBASIC program, the lower down it extends, and if you ever manage to produce the 'Out of memory' error report then this means that the SuperBASIC and heap areas have collided, leaving no free space in the middle.

Under normal circumstances, there will be quite a bit of space between the data areas. The QL takes advantage of this by making temporary copies of open files in the gap. The data can then be accessed more quickly. This goes some way to explaining why microdrive files should always be closed after use — any changes made might not be contained on the microdrive cartridge itself.

It is important to distinguish between the physical memory map of the QL and the rather more mobile 'software' memory map controlled by QDOS. Certain features will never move, and these comprise the physical map. The main ROM, for example, will always be found in the same place. I/O addresses are decoded by hardware, so these will always be the same. As a word of warning, Sinclair make no promises that later models of machines will have precisely the same I/O map; they recommend that all references to I/O be made via the correct SuperBASIC commands (ie don't PEEK the clock direct, use DATE) or, if using machine code, the QDOS traps. Obviously, any hardware changes would be accompanied by the appropriate changes to the ROM, so, by observing the above rules, software should remain compatible with later types of QL. Having said that, the I/O addresses certainly are part of the physical map of your computer: if you want to change them you will need, at the very least, a soldering iron!

CHAPTER 10
The Video Display

The display produced by the QL can be genuinely described as high resolution colour. There are two modes available (briefly mentioned in Chapter 5), and both have the same vertical resolution of 256 pixels. The 512 (high) mode, as its name implies, has a horizontal resolution of 512 pixels: it can produce one of four colours for each dot — black, red, green and white. The lower mode, 256, has only half the horizontal resolution but has eight colours — blue, magenta, cyan and yellow, in addition to the above four.

Both modes use virtually the whole screen area, which leads to the problem of overscanning when a domestic TV is used: some of the screen image will 'fall off' the sides, top and bottom of the television, although the amount lost will vary from set to set. The QL takes this into account in its software, setting limits in the TV mode to ensure that all printing is visible. The monitor mode, which uses 512 pixel resolution, assumes that a high quality monitor is in use.

The ZX8302

The mechanism for producing the display is contained within the ZX8302 chip, the master chip or video chip. This is a custom-built device — you will not find it listed in any electronics catalogue! The chip has many inputs and outputs, including address and data lines for accessing the screen memory area, and crystal-controlled oscillator circuits from which it times its operations.

The screen images the chip produces come from the screen memory area, placed there by the CPU. The master chip (MC) takes this information and translates it into real-time analogue, colour and sync signals that can be fed into a monitor. The provision for feeding a television or 'composite video' type of monitor involves coding the signal to the PAL (phase alternate line) format. This is achieved using a Motorola integrated circuit, the MC 1377, which contains all the necessary circuitry to convert RGB and sync signals into either PAL (the UK standard) or NTSC (American) composite video. The video is now suitable to drive a composite monitor or, via the QL's modulator, a television. Let's follow through the process involved.

The MC generates the frame and line synchronising pulses required to lock up the display. After a frame pulse and the first line pulse, the monitor or TV will be aiming its beam at the top lefthand side of its screen. The chip now requires information as to which analogue signal it should be producing at this moment: it uses its address and data lines to read the first two words from the screen area of RAM (normally 20000h). We will look at how the information is coded in a moment.

The MC decodes the data and now has enough information to generate the first section of the first line. In fact, although the chip only knows what ⅟64th of the line should be, the time that this portion of the analogue signal lasts is sufficient for the next long word of data to be fetched. So we have the chip, acting independently of the CPU, fetching, decoding and passing on the video information. When the MC has produced a line — the timescale of which is carefully controlled — it sends out a line pulse to force the display attached to fly back to the start of the next line. This process is repeated 256 times, once for each vertical line. The 625 line TV standard actually has 287 (and a half!) active picture lines per field, so there is a small gap at the bottom of the TV display — this may be noticeable on some televisions. Having transmitted one field, a second, interlaced, field is produced in the same manner.

Controlling the ZX8302

'But what happens if the CPU and the video chip both want to access the screen RAM at the same time?' I hear you ask. This would be quite a likely occurrence if special arrangements were not made. The master chip needs priority over the CPU to ensure a stable, snow-free display.

The QL overcomes this problem by using a design feature of the CPU. The 68008 is equipped with asynchronous control lines for addressing memory. When it has sent out the correct signals to the buses, the 68008 waits for the control line DTACK to be asserted before collecting data or assuming a write operation has been completed. By not asserting DTACK, external hardware can cause the CPU to 'hang on' while it makes use of the memory. This is precisely what the hardware of the QL does — not only is the screen information collected in this way, but the refresh operations necessary for dynamic RAM chips are also supplied. To allow both the CPU and MC to share the address and data bus, multiplexing chips (74LS257s) are included in the QL design (although not included in the diagrams in this book).

The master chip can be controlled by software, as it is addressed through a memory-mapped port arrangement — the processor can write data to the MC as if it were a memory location. The circuitry is so arranged that writing to address 18063h will input three signals into the MC; these are passed along bits 1, 3 and 7 of the data bus. This is a common way of interfacing other hardware with microprocessors and means that special instructions are not required; the port address is treated as a location in the memory map which performs special tasks.

The CPU can cause the display to be switched off and on via bit 1 of the data passed to the MC. Writing a 1 to this bit will cause the screen display to go blank. By resetting bit 1 to 0, the picture is restored. This facility may be of some use: for example, you may wish to blank out the screen while a complex picture is drawn. To see what happens, try entering the following line of SuperBASIC in TV mode:

POKE 98403,2 : PAUSE 100 : POKE 98403,8

The last poke of the above line gives a clue to another control that the CPU has over the master chip. Bit 3 determines which of the two video modes is used to generate the display. If a 0 is poked to bit 3 of 18063h, then a high resolution 512 picture is produced: poking 1 to bit 3 will cause the low resolution 256 mode to be brought into operation, altering the manner in which screen data is decoded. With your QL in TV mode, try POKE 98403,0. The patterning is caused because screen bit patterns vary between modes. The reverse process demonstrates this also — reset the computer, select the monitor mode and enter POKE 98403,8. The bit patterns of the command left on the screen contain data that causes the flash facility to come into operation. Note that the system software is completely in the dark about what you have done — in both cases it will continue to provide the 'wrong' data for the screen, and all the window and character sizes will be left over from the previous mode.

The CPU can also control video generation by altering the base address of the memory map. The normal base, 20000h, is selected by poking a 0 to bit 7 of 18063h. However, try POKE 98403,128. What has happened? The MC is now using a different area as its data for the screen, and you will now be looking at memory locations 28000h to 2FFFFh. This does not make much of a sensible picture — what you can see are the system variables, tables, and the common heap area. If you hold down a key you should be able to see the queue of keyboard data alter. (The number of rapidly changing dots shows that, even when doing nothing, your QL is still busy!) Try typing in PAUSE 1000 — some, but not all, of the activity stops. The regular patterns are the blocks of memory which, although reserved, have not been filled with data. You can also see some work going on if you enter, with the second screen selected, DIM a(20000). At first the blocks will be altered but, after 15 seconds or so, the Super-BASIC area will appear at the bottom of the screen and make its way towards the heap area. After the two areas have bumped into each other, try typing POKE 98403,0. If you manage to return to the normal display, you will find the 'Out of memory' error message awaiting you.

There is no way of making use of the facility for two screens from SuperBASIC, because you can't poke bit patterns or load bytes from microdrive into the top part of the second screen — if you try, you will corrupt the system variables and tables. However, the use of a second screen could be a great asset to graphic programs, even though it would consume 32K of memory. Two possible approaches to the problem are writing in machine code that ignores QDOS (and disables the interrupts), or taking advantage of the fact that the OS uses relative addressing for its accesses to the system variables. This second possibility would involve moving the system variables to a higher address, as well as requiring an intimate knowledge of QDOS. Another warning — at the time of writing, no official Sinclair documentation mentions the second screen facility, so it might disappear on later versions of the QL!

The screen display

Having made the CPU force a few tricks on the video chip, it is now time to look at how the screen display is actually coded in memory. The layout of the screen has been demonstrated by the machine code routine in Chapter 8: the first word address relates to the top lefthand corner of the screen, and each subsequent word relates to further along the first screen line. Having reached the end of the first line, the next word address relates to the lefthand end of the next line, and so on to the end of the screen. In fact, the word order is the same as the scanning pattern of a video display coded into memory, ignoring any interlacing. The manner in which the individual bits of the words are used differs between the two modes. First of all, we will look at the high resolution four-colour mode.

High resolution

Each dot or pixel of the screen has two bits of memory allocated to it in 512 mode. If we split the word into two bytes, the bit numbers used are the same for each pixel. The most significant bit, ie 7, of each byte is used to store the information for the left most pixel for which the word is responsible: bit 6 is tied to the next pixel to the right, and so on. In fact, the layout of pixels is the same as the layout of a binary number.

If we take the two bits of the pixel, it is possible, using the principles of binary, to generate one of four codes. The bit from the low byte, or, if you think in terms of words, the most significant of the two bits (as words start with the low byte), is called the 'green' bit. The other bit is the 'red' bit. If both bits are zero, then the MC translates that pixel as black. If either bit is set, then the pixel assumes the colour that their names imply. If both bits are set then some cheating is required: when you mix red and green light you obtain yellow light, but the video chip ignores the rules of colour mixing by producing a white pixel.

To give an example of this organisation, we can construct a simple pattern, poke it to the screen and observe the result. The desired pattern is two pixels each of black, green, red and white. Therefore, the binary pattern of the low byte is 00110011; for the generation of both green and white the green bits must be set. The high byte needs to be 00001111 bin. Thus we have the hexadecimal values 33h and 0Fh. Reset your QL and select the monitor mode. We will poke the values into the listing area of the screen, hex addresses 24010h and 24011h. First enter POKE 147472,51. Two green dots should appear, each being two pixels wide. Now enter POKE 147473,15: black will emerge to the left, a red dot will appear after the first green dot, while the second will become white and merge with the background.

Low resolution

The lower resolution, eight-colour mode follows a linear organisation. The bit pattern of the two bytes, 16 bits in all, only needs supply data for four pixels, so each pixel has four bits allocated to it, two in each byte. Bits 7 and 6 relate to pixel 1, bits 5 and 4 to pixel 2, etc. To supply the eight values required for the colours, three bits are all that are needed; the fourth bit is used to signify the flash state. First, the colours — in the low byte bit 7 is the green bit, and in the high byte bit 7 is the red and bit 6 the blue bits of the leftmost pixel (pixel 1). The process follows the laws of additive colour mixing: if no bits are set, black; all bits set, white; any individual bit produces its own colour; as for combinations of any two bits, red and green give yellow, green and blue produce cyan, and red and blue result in magenta.

The fourth bit in memory signals the video chip to toggle the flash state. When this bit is 0, then no change is carried out, but when it is 1, the flash state is inverted, that is, switched on when off and vice versa. When the flash has been turned on, it affects itself and all subsequent pixels in the rest of the screen line. The internal circuitry of the MC now switches, at the rate of about three times a second, between continuing to decode the screen data normally, and using the colour of the 'flash on' pixel as the screen data. This behaviour continues until either another flash bit is encountered or the end of the screen line is reached, when the hardware automatically turns the flash mode off.

Four pixels of white, for example, which all leave the flash state unaffected, will have the binary pattern 1010101011111111, or AAAAFFFFh. Using the formula GFGFGFGFRBRBRBRB, which represents the bit pattern for one word, you may like to try poking your own predictions to the TV screen. Don't forget that you can use the Monitor program to change memory locations. You will find experimenting with hex values quicker: if you are not quite clear about the flash facility, then a few trials (and errors!) should soon fix the system in your mind.

Printing characters

The way in which characters appear on the screen involves no more hardware than I have already described — *software* is the power behind the many printing features of the QL. The parts of the operating software which deal with character output alone are both complex and flexible. The same main routines take account of such factors as print positioning, colours, character size, underlining and exotic facilities such as OVER −1. However, at the core of the system exists a routine which, in its simplest role, converts an ASCII value passed to it in a register into a binary pattern in the screen memory map, and therefore on the video display.

The main tool used in this process is a table of data called, on the QL, a 'fount'. Other microcomputers normally make do with the title 'character shape table' or such like, but as the QL can possess two such tables for each screen window, the grander name of fount seems appropriate.

The first two bytes of each fount contain two pieces of information that relate to the number of characters in the table. Byte 1 is the ASCII value of the lowest printable character: this is normally 1Fh, not 20h (the space character) as you might think. The next byte holds a value which is the number of valid characters in the table, minus one. The default value here is 60h (96 dec), which means that there are 41h (65 dec) printable characters. If you take a look at the character set section of your QL manual, you will see that this is one more than the number of available characters. Ask your computer to PRINT CHR$ (31), and you will see the shape stored at the first location.

The rest of the fount table holds nine bytes for each character. The smallest character size in each mode takes a block of pixels 10 high by 6 pixels wide: allowing a one-pixel margin between characters means that the shapes themselves are 9 by 5. A nine-byte entry in the table holds the binary pattern for each row of the character, with bits 6 to 2 each containing a binary one for paper, and zero for ink.

Back to the printing routine — or at least, my simplified version of it. It checks the supplied character code against the information at the beginning of the first fount. If the code is too low or high, the routine checks the second fount, and if the code fails the test again, the printing routine uses the lowest shape of the second fount. This explains the occurrence of that unusual shape you get when you ask the computer to print an unprintable character: the QL has only one fount in ROM, but both pointers for each channel point to it, so the 1Fh character is the final default. On the other hand, if a valid character has been passed to the print routine, the routine must locate the correct pattern. It does this by subtracting the lowest valid value from the code, and multiplying the remainder by nine, the number of bytes per shape. Now, by adding the base address plus 2 (to bypass the size data) the routine knows where to find the pattern of the desired character.

With the six-bit wide shape now available to the print routine, it can set about poking it to the screen. The current cursor position of the screen is calculated and a section of each line of pixels is fetched from the screen. A suitable mask pattern is calculated to make the required 'hole' and then, using the mask, shape data and colour information from the window data tables, the pixel information is modified to create one line of the character before it is returned to its original location in memory. This process is repeated for each screen line it is necessary to alter in order to create the character. Remember that the QL can have up to four different character sizes; the larger letters are simply magnified versions of the smaller letters, produced for example, by printing one character line to two lines of pixels in order to produce double-height characters.

User-definable characters

One feature that is missing from the QL's SuperBASIC is the ability to define your own character shapes. However, it is quite possible, with the application of a little machine code, to create extra shapes that can be printed using PRINT, without using complex drawing procedures. The new shapes will also conform to all the usual printing instructions and therefore offer possibilities for graphic games, or special symbols in more serious applications.

You may have noticed that I did not give an address at which you can find the default fount table in the ROM. This is the sort of information that is likely to change as alterations are made to the operating software; any address given will only be valid for one particular batch of machines. We can find the fount by a little investigation, and the process will help to clarify how user-defined characters can be implemented.

Load the Monitor program — if you do not enter it, then you will need to do quite a bit of PEEKing and number conversion. Use the Examine Memory option to look at address 28078h. This is a system variable location, which is used by QDOS to store the address of the base of the 'channel table' (a table of data at the bottom end of the memory map which holds a further series of addresses). At 28078h to 2807Bh (known as SV_CHBAS), you will find the long word address of this channel table, which my QL, with the monitor loaded, makes out to be 28B60h. Remember that you may find a different address: there is no compulsion for the channel table to remain in the same place. We now know the address of the start of the channel table, so use the monitor to look at the table by examining 28B60h or whatever address you found in SV_ CHBAS.

You are now looking at a list of addresses, each taking up four bytes. Each address points to another table of data which holds the information required to implement each open channel. With the monitor program installed there will be four open channels, each with its table of data stored in memory: the first four long words of the channel table will therefore contain four valid addresses, each pointing to a 'channel definition block'. After the four valid pointers, the long word entries in the rest of the table all begin with the byte FFh — this is used to signal to the operating system that the channel is not open. Try breaking out of the monitor program and OPENing a few channels — eg OPEN #6,SER1 and OPEN #7,SER2 (on early QLs you may need to use CLEAR first). Now re-run the monitor program and re-examine the table. You will find two further entries, pointing to newly set-up channel definition blocks. If you now break out and CLOSE #7, re-run the program and look at the table again, you should find that the table entry for channel 7 has been prefixed with FFh.

Notice that, in the above example, we did not open channel 5. Nevertheless, a gap was not left in the table for the unopened channel. If you would like to try OPEN #5,SER2, you will find the new entry is made at the end of the table. At the same time, any closed channel entries are purged from the table. From this, we can deduce that the operating system does not rely on the channel table being in order, but searches the whole table for a matching channel number each time. It is therefore ever so slightly quicker if channels are opened in the order of their frequency of use — less time will be spent searching for channels that are at the top of the list.

Now that we have investigated the channel tables, it is time to look at the definition blocks themselves. Examine the addresses pointed to by the first channel table entry, channel 0 (28E00h on my QL). The first 18h bytes hold the same data, whether the block is a channel definition, or other types of definition blocks. The first long word holds the length of the data block in bytes: this may well be 100h, which is the default value. Next comes an address which points to the machine code routine that 'drives' the channel or whatever. This will normally be a vector of the routine in ROM responsible for handling whatever sort of channel is being defined. Channel 0 is a console channel, which is to say it is both an input and output channel; it will have a different driver routine than, say, a serial channel. QDOS uses the third word to indicate if the block has an owner job. This is a part of the multi-tasking system, so if no value is present here it means that this definition block is free-standing. The fourth long word gives the address that is to be set when the definition block is removed from RAM: if you trace this back, you will discover that it is the address of the byte that is set to FFh when a channel is closed (don't try this with channel 0!). The next data is only a word in length and is the number of the channel. The rest of the first 18h bytes are used by the time-sharing elements of QDOS.

So the first block (28E00h to 28E17h) contains general-purpose data items to be used by the definition block; if you remember, we are looking for the fount address, which is contained in the next section of the table. This is a window data block, because channel 0 uses a window of the screen to print to. It starts at a position plus 18h bytes into the table, and contains all the data necessary to maintain a printing window on the screen. The words at +18h and +20h define the top lefthand side of the window; +1Ch and 1Eh the window size; the border width is held in +20h; and the cursor position and increment at +22h to +29h.

Finally, we have reached what we are looking for — at plus 2Ah bytes from the start of the channel definition block are two long word addresses that point to the founts. On my QL, I find the address 271Ah duplicated. You should also find two identical addresses, although they may be different from mine.

To summarise, we found the fount address by looking up the address of the channel tables in the system variable SV_CHBAS (28078h). Here we found the address of channel 0's definition block. Adding 2Ah to this gave us the address at which we could find the addresses of the founts used by the channel 0 window.

Now look at the fount in ROM. First you will find the code of the lowest printable character. Next comes the number, minus one, of characters that are printable. Finally comes the binary dot patterns, nine bytes at a time, for each shape. The first pattern is the unprintable character shape, followed by nine zero bytes for space, then the exclamation mark and so on.

The next program, Program 10.1, allows the addition of a number of user-defined characters. The trick it uses is to set up a second fount table in RAM that has a lower 'lowest printable code' value than the default table in ROM. The address of this second table is placed in the second fount address in the window definition block of the channel where we want to generate the custom shapes. Now, by using PRINT CHR$ (x), where x is a previously unprintable character in the range 16 to 31 decimal, the appropriate shape from our own RAM table will be used to form the character. All the normal functions, colour, size and so on, will continue as usual.

A wealth of peeks and pokes to find and alter the fount pointers may cause unforeseen problems, so the program uses the method recommended by Sinclair Research — that is, a QDOS trap to perform operations involving the I/O system. These will be explained in greater depth in Chapter 12. The effect is the same, but it actually involves less work from us. Enter Program 10.1 and save it before running it.

Program 10.1: User Defined Graphics

```
100 REMark  User Defined Graphics
110 MODE 8
120 start=RESPR(0)
130 IF start>262143 THEN start=RESPR(256)
140 RESTORE
150 check=0
160 FOR routine=0 TO 18 STEP 2
170   READ a$
180   word=dec(a$)
190   IF word<0 THEN bad_data
200   check=check+word
210   POKE_W start+routine,word
220 END FOR routine
230 IF check<>134046 THEN bad_data
240 table=start+20
250 REPeat shapes
260   READ a$
270   IF a$="end" THEN EXIT shapes
280   word=dec(a$)
290   IF word<0 THEN bad_data
300   POKE_W table,word
310   table=table+2
320 END REPeat shapes
330 CALL start
340 CLS:AT 10,10
350 PRINT "CHR$ (16 to 30)"\,
360 FOR udg=16 TO 30
370   PRINT CHR$(udg);
380 END FOR udg
390 STOP
400 REMark ------------------------------
410 DEFine FuNction dec(a$)
420   LOCal p,t,v%:t=0
430   FOR p=1 TO LEN(a$)
440     v%=CODE(a$(p))
450     IF v%>57 AND v%<65 THEN RETurn -1
455     IF v%<48 OR v%>70 THEN RETurn -1
460     t=t*16+v%-48-7*(v%>57)
470   END FOR p
480   RETurn t
490 END DEFine dec
500 REMark ---------------------------
510 DEFine PROCedure bad_data
520   PRINT #0,"Bad data":STOP
530 END DEFine bad_data
540 REMark -------------------------
550 REMark Machine code data
560 DATA "7025"
570 REMark MOVEQ #25,DO
580 REMark 25 is the number of the
```

136

```
582 REMark change fount routine
590 DATA "7600"
600 REMark CLR D3
610 REMark timeout=0
620 DATA "207C","1","1"
630 REMark MOVE.L #00010001,A0
640 REMark channel number into A0
650 DATA "2243"
660 REMark CLR A1
670 REMark fount 1 is default
680 DATA "45FA","6"
690 REMark LEA 6(PC),A2
700 REMark fount 2 is new table
710 DATA "4E43"
720 REMark TRAP 3
730 DATA "4E75"
740 REMark RTS
750 REMark end of routine
760 REMark start of table
770 DATA "100E"
780 REMark table header
790 DATA "4438","1010","1010"
794 DATA "5438","1010","3854"
796 DATA "1010","1010","3844"
800 REMark first two shapes
810 REMark insert further shapes here
820 DATA "end"
830 REMark end of table
```

When the program runs successfully, enter PRINT CHR$ (16). The result should be a downwards facing arrow. The new shapes will only appear on channel #1, the normal print output, but you may change this as you wish by altering the channel ID number contained in the code. Note this ID must be contained in both the low and high word of the long word supplied to the trap.

You will not get very far with two arrow shapes, which are all the program provides. The remark statements point out where you can insert further data in order to generate your own characters. The data is in hexadecimal form, as you will find that the best way to design shapes is as follows:

1. Draw a grid nine squares high by six squares wide on a piece of paper.
2. Fill in those that you require to be 'ink'.
3. Alongside each row write a binary number, left to right: the first digit should be (0), then write 0 for a paper square or 1 for ink. Finally, make the last digit a 0.
4. You should now have an eight-bit binary number for each of the nine rows of the shape. Convert each to hex by splitting it up into high and low nibbles and translating each of the four bits into a hex digit (this is good practice!).

137

5. The nine hex bytes should then be entered as data statements in the area of the program indicated by the remark statements.

The program reserves space for the fount table only on the first occasion that it is run. Once you are happy with the program and the shapes it produces, it can have the remarks deleted and be used as a PROC by merging it with other SuperBASIC programs. Alternatively, it may be loaded, run and then be erased by another program being loaded in its place — as the changes have already been made to the tables and the RESPR area is immune to CLEAR, the user-defined characters will remain until the computer is reset.

This chapter has looked at the rudiments of the display mechanism of the QL. How you use the knowledge depends on what you intend to use your computer for. At the simplest level, you now know what happens when you get your QL to print to the screen. If you intend to be more adventurous, then some of the QDOS traps described in Chapter 12 may be of interest. To achieve some stunning graphic effects, then machine code, a head for binary numbers, graph paper and patience are the order of the day!

CHAPTER 11
Input and Output

The terms 'input' and 'output' cover a number of areas of your QL's operation. The simplest example of the former is the SuperBASIC command INPUT: in this case the computer waits for you to type something into the machine via the keyboard. (The keyboard can also be read directly with the KEYROW function.) Other forms of input available on the QL are the serial RS232 ports, the microdrives and the networking ports. These can all be used to collect information from sources outside the computer. The CTL sockets are also a source of input: they are intended mainly for use with joysticks, although other devices could be plugged in. This facility is little more than an extension of the keyboard, as we shall see later in this chapter.

Output is most commonly encountered when something is printed on the screen. The error messages that appear at the bottom of the picture display are an example of computer-generated output, and whenever you use the PRINT command you are outputting information. The QL can also output information through the RS232 and network ports, or send it to the microdrives for storage. Another type of output is sound: the built-in speaker can generate a variety of noises, all under the control of Super-BASIC, but without tying up the main CPU for the duration of the sound.

The 8049 processor

The majority of low cost microcomputers contain only one microprocessor, which is responsible not only for running the programs presented to it, but also for sending information to, and collecting it from, the outside world. In some cases this process can be quite time-consuming. For example, the Sinclair Spectrum has a BEEP facility which ties up the CPU for the entire time that a sound is being produced. This means that, while a sound is being produced, the processor cannot read the keyboard. If the keyboard is not read frequently, then the computer may miss a vital keypress. The QL has overcome these disadvantages by employing a second microprocessor to handle input and, other than the screen display, output functions.

On the lefthand side of the QL's circuit board lives the 8049 single chip microprocessor. Whereas the main 68008 is a powerful and flexible chip, the 8049 is rather simple in operation. Yet it has other qualities that make it useful.

One of these is that it contains its own memory areas which are completely independent of the RAM and ROM that make up the QL's memory map. These cannot be accessed by the main CPU, which is good from the point of view of simplicity, but can make investigations rather difficult. The world inside the 8049 (or IPC — independent peripheral controller — as it is called) is a closed book as far as the 68008 is concerned — the main CPU just sends a command and lets the IPC get on with it. If the IPC wants to attract the attention of the 68008, it uses the interrupt lines to force the main processor to handle the information it has to pass on.

Contained within the 40-pin package of the 8049 are all the basic ingredients of an eight-bit microcomputer. A control unit supervises the fetching and execution of the instructions, and an ALU (arithmetic and logic unit) performs the binary arithmetic and logical operations necessary. There are a number of registers with special purposes. The program counter is 12 bits in size, and keeps track of the address, within the IPC's own memory map, of the current instruction. The IPC has an accumulator, and status and timer registers, while an eight-bit pointer holds addresses pertinent to the RAM area within the IPC memory map.

Notice that I haven't mentioned general-purpose address and data registers, of which the 68008 has so many. These registers are memory devices which the control unit can get at quickly, and normally consist of no more than RAM locations on the CPU chip which are specially addressed. The 8049 contains 128 bytes of RAM memory — 16 of these are used to provide two blocks of eight-byte registers. Either, but not both, of these register blocks may be active, and the IPC can switch between them at any time. Another area of internal RAM is reserved between the register areas for use as a simple stack.

One eighth of a kilobyte of random access memory may not sound very impressive when compared with the amount of RAM on board the QL, but the tasks which the IPC is designed to perform do not require much in the way of variable storage. The bulk of memory available is in the form of read only memory — 2K of instructions and data are etched permanently onto the chip. (I mentioned earlier that the PC is 12 bits in length, so it is possible for the 8049 to address 4K of memory in total, although the QL's design does not make use of this facility.) The 2K of program that is contained inside the IPC is what makes it behave the way it does. 8049 chips are used for many purposes (such as for printer controllers) and the process of programming the ROM sections of memory is part of the manufacturing process — if you replaced the 8049 in your QL with one which had a different program locked into it, the result would be a useless computer.

Communication with other devices is all handled through three eight-bit, bi-directional ports. Two of these are named ports 0 and 1, while the third is the data bus that would send and receive data if the memory map were extended outside the chip (the data bus is not implemented on the QL). These ports are decoded so that some appear in areas of the QL's main memory map; the 68008 can send and receive information as if the IPC were a memory location. Other bits of the ports are wired to enable them to assert the 68008 interrupt lines, while some can activate the serial driver circuits.

During the time your QL is switched on, two independent operations occur that occasionally interfere with each other. The main 68008 processor follows the operating system's instructions, carrying out a Super-BASIC program or running a machine code program such as Quill or Easel.

Whatever the main CPU is doing, the IPC is following its own in-built program. This is a machine code program — not written in 68008 code, of course, but in the machine code of the 8049. The instruction set, apart from being different, is also crude by comparison with that of the 68008. It takes a form similar to 8080 machine code — a chip that was a predecessor of the Z80 (this may account for early rumours that the QL, or ZX83 as it was code-named, was to contain a Z80 and would possibly be capable of running Spectrum software).

The program that the IPC runs is very repetitive — it constantly scans the keyboard for keypresses, keeps up the process of outputting data to drive the sound circuits, and monitors any input from the 68008 that requires attention. It may also handle the process of sending or receiving data via the serial channels and helping out the microdrives. The best way of viewing the IPC is as a very clever piece of hardware. It may be considered as a computer within a computer, but unfortunately we have no way of re-programing it. At least this saves us the trouble of understanding another breed of machine code!

The safest method of performing input and output tasks is by calling the QL's operating system, QDOS. All the possible input and output requirements can be achieved through the operating system — we will study QDOS in the next chapter. It is possible to use I/O calls (or TRAPs) that have a high level of sophistication, and so blithely instruct QDOS to send a chunk of information out of any open channel. Closer to the nuts and bolts of the system is a trap that sends direct commands to the IPC — once these commands have been received, the IPC will adjust the running of its internal program to respond to the request. The remainder of this chapter will take a general look at the I/O systems of the QL — refer to the next chapter to see how they are controlled, or how to use them in your own machine code applications.

The keyboard

The keyboard of any computer is the main interface with the user and, for this reason, the better the quality of the keyboard, the more pleasant a computer is to use. The QL possesses a full-size keyboard featuring moving keys, essential for applications such as word-processing.

The mechanical construction is a clever compromise between cost and performance. The keytops rest on a rubbery sheet which has raised bubbles at intervals corresponding to each key position. These give the keys their sprung feel and provide the feedback that allows the user to sense that the keys have 'made contact'. Beneath the rubber bubbles lies a membrane sheet which performs the electrical switching. This comprises a sandwich of plastic material containing electrically conductive tracks. Where these pass over each other they are insulated from each other, except in the regions directly beneath each key. At these points, applying pressure to the membrane causes two tracks to be bridged together, forming an electrical contact.

There are 65 keys, but the shift key is duplicated, so we actually have 64. This is a convenient number. If you have experimented with the KEYROW function you will know that the keys are arranged on an 8×8 grid: with eight input wires into the keyboard membrane, and an output of a further eight wires, there are 64 possible ways any one input can be short-circuited to any one output, one for each key — this is how the IPC scans the keyboard to see if a key is pressed. Both the KEYROW function and the normal keyscan employ the same technique. The normal scan is more complex, checking each row in turn and converting the results into an ASCII code. In addition, shift, CTRL and ALT are taken into account, but these are software complications to what is a simple electrical process.

Let us look at KEYROW (0). If you turn to the description of this function in the keyword section of the manual, there is a table showing the row layout of the keys. From this you can see that row 0 contains the five function keys and the numbers 4, 5 and 7. When you request the value of KEYROW (0), the input to row 0 is asserted. The eight output conductors are fed back into the IPC as eight separate bits, one for each column. This information consists of a byte of which the individual bits will be asserted only if the column connector (or strobe line) has made contact with an asserted row connector.

Therefore, if no key in the row is pressed, zero is returned to the IPC from the keyboard output columns. Function key 4 is connected to column 0, or bit 0 of the byte read into the IPC — if F4 is pressed, then row 0 is connected to column 0. The value returned is 00000001 bin, 1 decimal. At the other end of the scale, number 7 key is connected to column 7. If this key is pressed then KEYROW (0) will return 10000000 bin, 128 decimal. If both these keys are pressed then the result is 10000001 bin, 129 decimal. From the above examples, and by studying the table in the manual, you can see how pressing any individual key will return a unique result.

The manual hints at some of the problems which can occur with this matrix layout. It is possible that with more than two keys pressed, spurious results may occur. One unavoidable 'bug' can be demonstrated with the following short line of SuperBASIC:

REPEAT loop : AT 0,0 : PRINT KEYROW (1)

Enter the line as a command. The value 0 should appear at the top of the screen. When you press ENTER the zero will turn into a 1. Now continue to hold down the ENTER key and also hold down the function keys, one at a time. F1, F2 and F3 each held down in conjunction with ENTER will still result in 1 being displayed, but when you add F4 the displayed result will change to 27!

The reason for this is that F4 and ENTER are both attached to column 0. The asserting signal passes along row 1 and is passed to column 0 when ENTER is pressed. If F4 is also pressed, the signal is passed on to row 0 as well as row 1. Therefore the other keys attached to row 0 have been activated accidentally and will pass this signal on to their appropriate column outputs if they are also pressed. If you release the ENTER key, the result reverts to zero as the asserting signal is no longer leaking on to the wrong row.

The normal keyscanning routine that the IPC performs is capable of storing up to seven keypresses before it needs to pass them on to the main CPU. This can be proved by disabling the interrupts and then performing a long machine code delay loop. When the QL is returned to Super-BASIC and it encounters a STOP command, the first seven letters pressed during the delay will appear at the bottom of the screen. Instead of giving you the code to try this experiment, I will provide the information you need and let you practise your machine code writing skills. To disable the interrupts, you must enter supervisor mode. This can be achieved with TRAP 0, which returns with an RTS rather than an RTE — don't forget to end with an RTE to return to user mode. The interrupt mask must be set to 111 with the MOVE to SR instruction, and then a long delay can be created with a DBRA (DBF) instruction.

At the prompting of interrupts received from the IPC, the 68008 takes keypress information and places it in a queue of data in the table area of RAM. The 68008 also handles the auto-repeat and CAPS LOCK functions, so these can be tampered with by altering certain system variables.

If CAPS LOCK is activated, then address 28088h (163976 dec) will return FFh, otherwise it will return zero. So if you poke any value other than zero into this system variable, caps lock will be switched on — zero will switch it off.

The auto-repeat can also be altered. To change the length of delay before a key begins to repeat, alter the value of the word in address 2808Ch (163980 dec). This is normally set to 1Eh; lowering it will shorten the delay, increasing it will lengthen it. The frequency of the repetition after the initial delay is controlled by the value in 2808Eh (again, word length): 2808Eh normally contains 4, but you may increase it to reduce the frequency.

There are two QDOS traps which are used to read the keyboard, one working like KEYROW and the other fetching a stored keypress from the IPC. These are detailed in the next chapter.

The CTL sockets

The CTL sockets into which you may plug joysticks are simply extensions of the keyboard matrix. CTL 1 simulates the cursor keys, with the space bar used as fire. CTL 2 is linked to keyrow 0: F1 is left, F2 down, F3 fire, F4 up and F5 right. The sockets are fed with the appropriate keyrow input and the five other pins are returned to the relevant key column.

The wiring pattern is as follows. With the socket facing you so that you can read the label, from left to right the output pins are: fire, up, down, right and left. At the far right of the socket is the keyrow column connector. If you have a joystick which you wish to wire up (and can obtain the necessary type of plug), then the above information should help you get it right first time. However, if you make a mistake or are unsure of how the joystick itself is wired up, no damage should occur from trial and error, as a joystick is a purely passive device.

Sound

The sound facilities of the QL are not as good as some of the more games-orientated computers, which tend to have special sound generating chips which allow the build-up of complex effects. The QL just relies on the IPC, which is capable of producing a broad range of sounds, for the noises it can make.

One bit of the 8049's output is attached to amplification circuitry which drives the small speaker mounted underneath the microdrives. The IPC is therefore capable of toggling the loudspeaker by switching this bit high or low, and can do this at such a speed that audio frequencies are produced. You may think that the sounds produced will be rather square, but at the higher frequencies this is cured by components in the amplification stages that round off the sharp edges of the sound waves generated. The program in the IPC needs to run at a fixed time interval for the accurate reproduction of tones, but this has no effect on the main computer.

This is how a simple tone is produced. The IPC sets its output to the speaker high. It then has time to kill, depending on the frequency of the tone it is trying to reproduce, but it can put this time to good use running other programs. When the allotted time has passed, the output is forced low for a further duration, by which time the IPC has produced one cycle of a sound wave. This rather crude approach explains the poor results of the lower pitched notes. Try BEEP 0,255: this actually sounds like a square wave, while BEEP 0,0 generates quite an acceptable sine wave.

The additional parameters that BEEP can expect are implemented by software within the IPC. For example, the fuzzy parameter uses the IPC's own random number generating software to introduce small variations to the pitch of a note on its way between two specified notes. Mastering the BEEP command is really a case of trial and error: a scientific approach can be used, but the interaction between the various parameters and the crude tone-generating system means that the unexpected is likely to happen. BEEP can be used from machine code with the help of QDOS.

RS232 and networks

The 8049 IPC has other roles to play in the input and output facilities of the QL. The serial RS232 and network ports both employ a form of transmission and reception which handles data as a binary stream of information. This is the basic distinction between the serial interfaces of the QL and parallel methods (such as the Centronics type of printer interface) which use more than one data line to send individual bits simultaneously.

RS232-C is a defined standard to which many pieces of equipment conform. Unfortunately there are many variations possible, both in the way that the connections are wired up and the speed of transmission. The basic principle is the use of a pair of wires, one held at ground voltage (zero volts), and the other going high if a 1 is being transmitted or staying low for a 0. After a period of time which depends on the transmission speed, the wire takes on the level of the next bit, and so on. The first bit sent is a start bit, then eight bits are sent which are either all data (eight-bit ASCII) or include one used as a parity bit (seven-bit ASCII). Finally, one or two stop bits are normally used to signify the end of one character of data. The parity bit is used as a check to ensure that data is not corrupted — for example, if even parity is being used, then the parity bit will be set if the sum of the other bits is even.

In addition to the various formats which can be assumed, the speed at which the data is transmitted can vary. The rate of transmission is measured in bits per second, a unit of measurement called 'baud'. The slowest baud rate that the QL can work at is 75. At these low speeds, RS232 interfaces are very reliable and can work along considerable distances without the danger of electrical interference. However, at these speeds the system is working slower than a good typist! The QL can also work at various speeds up to 9600 baud, and is capable of transmitting, but not receiving, at 19200 baud.

One problem which can arise is that of printers which can receive data into a RAM buffer. Quite a lot of information can be passed at high speed, but once the buffer is full, further information sent will be lost. Additionally, some devices may be able to receive at a speed that does not match any of the transmission rates available. A technique called 'handshaking' is employed to overcome these problems. The receiving end of the link sends a signal back to the sending end along additional CTS (clear to send) or DTR (data terminal ready) lines that can be negated, ie pulled low, in order to halt the stream of information. Only when the line is re-asserted will the transmissions be continued.

What with varying bit patterns and baud rates, and optional handshaking, the so-called 'standard' is not looking much like a standard. A further complication arises because a computer, modem, printer, or whatever can be wired as either a terminal or a communicator. Either type can send or receive, but they do so along different pins. A terminal device sends data out on the transmit line (TxD) and receives data on the receive line: a communicator does the opposite. If a terminal wishes for a pause in the data being sent, it negates the DTR line: a communication device uses a CTS line for this purpose.

The designers of the QL have gone to great lengths to solve the compatibility problems of using RS232 interfaces. The two serial sockets SER1 and SER2 work differently, SER1 as a communicator and SER2 as a terminal. Software provisions allow different parity and baud rates, and handshaking is optional. The pin allocation, from right to left as you face the socket, is GND (0v), TxD, RxD, DTR, CTS, and +12 volts.

The IPC's role in the RS232 port operation is that of a software interface. Up to 25 characters can be held in a buffer and only when the buffer is full in the case of receive, or empty in the case of transmit, does the main CPU need to pay attention. The baud and format variations are all taken care of by software, while the master chip helps out on the hardware side. The end of the QL's RS232 chain comprises two special chips: an MC 1489 contains four driving circuits that convert the TTL signals of the computer to the electrical standards of the RS232 standard; an MC 1488, containing four receivers, does the opposite.

Networking is a simple system, by comparison, as all the computers on the network share the same standards. It is again a serial system — the networking facility relies on software to identify who is trying to talk to whom over the shared 'loop' of binary wire. No handshaking is involved.

146

Microdrives

The QL possesses a form of data storage that is unique to Sinclair Research — the microdrive. The principles of magnetic recording, covered in Chapter 1, are still applicable; it is the layout of the system that is unusual. Cassette recorders are often used by home computers to store programs and data, and this keeps costs very low. The disadvantages of a cassette system are that they are slow and do not have random access. A domestic audio cassette recorder runs the magnetic tape across the head at the slowest speed at which it is possible to reproduce audio signals: this means that 1500 baud is the highest speed of data recording possible with any degree of reliability. Modifying a standard mechanism to increase the speed still leaves the problem of finding data quickly. Floppy disks offer a much better alternative in this respect as they are arranged like a record — the magnetic recording consists of concentric circles on the face of a flat disk, so by moving the head across the surface of the revolving disk a different track can be found quickly. However, it is not cheap to produce a disk drive, which has a moveable head assembly which must be moved within very fine tolerances.

The microdrive has quite a simple assembly. The record and replay head is fixed, and there is not even a moving pinch wheel. When the cartridge is pushed into the drive, the tape it contains is sandwiched between the spindle of the drive motor and a plastic roller contained in the cartridge case. Apply power to the motor and it revolves, dragging the endless loop of high-grade magnetic tape past the head. The length of the loop is about 17 feet, arranged around a single spool. The speed of the drive is such that the complete loop passes over the head in around seven seconds, giving a tape-to-head speed of about 30 inches per second (ips). By comparison, a standard cassette mechanism runs at one and seven eighths ips, 16 times slower.

The signals recorded on the cartridge are single bits of data. Before a cartridge is used it must be formatted, which involves recording test blocks of 256 bytes on the tape and then verifying the recording. Any blocks which fail the test are discarded and a map of the sectors available is made. This map is the crux of the operating system, and it is copied into RAM for quick access. The individual blocks are now available for storing data, the gaps between each block being important as a means of finding the next block. If a particular block is deleted, the entry in the map is altered. Free blocks are simply over-recorded when the QL wishes to store some data.

The microdrive assemblies are separate from the main circuit board of the QL. The electrical connections are via a 16-way ribbon cable soldered to a dual in-line pin arrangement: the assemblies can therefore be replaced fairly simply if they should fail. Each microdrive has its own custom-built chip, a ULA (uncommitted logic array), that handles the

147

drive: the ULA interfaces with the IPC and I/O map, controls the recording and replay process and switches the motor. Apart from the ULA, each microdrive contains a voltage regulator and a handful of passive components.

It is this efficient construction, along with the high software element involved in the operation of the microdrives, that keeps the cost of manufacture low. The cost of the cartridges themselves is dictated by the economics of scale — they should be little more expensive to produce than high quality audio cassettes, but demand needs to be high for the price to become comparable. The 100K capacity of each microdrive gives the QL a great deal of storage, quickly accessible.

CHAPTER 12
Software Maketh the Machine

It is no use sitting down in front of your QL and typing 'Play me a cheerful tune' — it simply won't know what you're talking about. You can write a program that will play any tune you like, but first of all you must learn how to make the computer understand you. In order to bridge the gap between machine code and human language, there have been developed over the years many intermediate languages that can be entered into computers and understood by both parties. The commonest language now used by microcomputers is BASIC, which is short for Beginners' All-purpose Symbolic Instruction Code. This language is easier to grasp than most others and, although 'professionals' are somewhat disparaging about it, it would not enjoy its popularity if it were not fairly flexible and powerful.

SuperBASIC

The QL is equipped with a greatly improved version which Sinclair Research have named SuperBASIC. SuperBASIC allows programmers to write programs that avoid most of the criticisms levelled at BASIC, with structured control commands, sensible variable names and recursive techniques all possible. It is still easy to write bad programs on the QL, but there are less excuses for doing so.

If you wish to use other languages, that is perfectly possible, but Super-BASIC is resident in the QL, and if you have not written programs before you will find it challenging enough to begin with. The manual gives a good grounding in the principles of using SuperBASIC; the finer points are outside the scope of this book.

How does a language work? The CPU of a computer only understands its own brand of machine code, not statements such as PRINT DATE$. Going back to our earlier example, imagine you have written two procedures to play tunes. 'PROC Happy_tune' pipes out the notes of 'Happy Birthday' and 'PROC Marching_tune' performs a passable rendition of 'Imperial Echoes'. We can create our own form of language interpreter with some lines of SuperBASIC:

10 INPUT A$

20 IF A$="play me a happy tune" THEN Happy_tune : STOP
30 IF A$="play me a marching tune" THEN Marching_tune : STOP
40 PRINT "I don't understand" : STOP

Very crude, but, to the uninitiated, typing 'play me a happy tune' elicits a seemingly intelligent response. What really happens is that the interpreter compares the command given to it with a list: if the interpreter recognises the command as one of the few phrases it knows, it will react.

That, at its most simplistic, is what a language interpreter does. Super-BASIC has a list of known commands and functions, and is programmed to react by invoking the correct piece of machine code. When you first switch on your QL, after the various setting-up routines you will enter the command mode of SuperBASIC. Whatever you type into the machine is stored until a line is completed by your pressing ENTER. The interpreter looks at the data entered, searching it for words it knows. If the first word is, for example, PRINT it will store this as a 'token', a word or more of coded data: this token would be stored as the first part of the line. The whole line is treated in a similar manner, and new variable names are entered in a table and given their own code. When the line has been successfully tokenised, it is stored in the SuperBASIC program area if it has a line number, or executed if it has not.

The process of tokenising the program saves memory space and speeds up the running of the program. SuperBASIC also speeds things up by compiling a table of relative addresses. This saves the time that other BASICs spend searching through the program for the next line to interpret.

QDOS

SuperBASIC is only part of the operating software. Many of the routines in the ROM are part of QDOS, which, although used by the interpreter, can also run independently. There are two main ways of using QDOS.

The more complex allows multi-tasking. This is achieved by holding two or more programs in the transient program area — these must be self-contained, user mode routines. QDOS runs one program for a period of time called a timeslice, and then uses an interrupt to gain control and allow the next program to run for a timeslice: this means that individual programs each get a share of the CPU's time.

The second approach to QDOS is as a collection of routines that can be called from a user's machine code program — the complex I/O operations can be performed this way. To use the first approach to QDOS requires detailed information, and at the time of writing Sinclair have not published a QDOS manual. The second use of the operating system, to save us re-inventing the wheel, can be explored. What follows is a look at the most useful routines, and how they can be put to use.

There are two methods of calling QDOS routines from your own machine code. The main method involves the use of the 68008 TRAP instruction. As explained in Chapter 7, this is a method of generating software-induced exceptions. There are 16 possible traps; each has a long word space reserved in the vector table which holds the address of a routine to handle the exception. For example, if the processor encounters a TRAP 0 instruction, it goes into supervisor mode, stacks the status register and PC, and then jumps to the address held in vector 32 (address 80h), which is the first entry in the table of trap vectors. As the CPU is now in supervisor mode, the SSP is used for stack operations and an RTE instruction is required to return to the calling program.

In addition to using TRAP, some ROM routines are accessible via vector addresses stored from C0h upwards in the exception table. This area is designated 'Unassigned, Reserved' by Motorola. Both these methods ensure that no direct call need ever be made to the routines — if they are relocated in later versions of the ROM, software using the trap and vector methods will still be able to find the desired routine, as the vector table will reflect the changes.

Traps

The first trap we will look at has already been mentioned, trap 0. This is the only easy way of entering supervisor mode. All it does is alter the SSP to point to the return address and perform an RTS. The code for TRAP 0 is 4E40h. To return to user mode (and therefore be able to use RTS and return to a previous calling program — ie SuperBASIC) use MOVE #0,SR. The code for this is 46FC,0.

There are four further traps which you can use, but the first three of these can perform a number of functions. Trap 1 invokes the 'manager' routines, trap 2 opens and closes channels, and trap 3 performs input and output functions. Trap 4 is for the use of the SuperBASIC interpreter, and makes parameters passed to further traps relative to A6. The various subdivisions of traps 1, 2 and 3 can be selected by loading data register 0 with a value which will dictate the action taken. Other values are also supplied by passing them in the registers.

Trap 1

My first example of using one of the multiple choice traps is a simple one to illustrate the principles. Loading D0 with 0 and then performing trap 1 calls the manager routine which returns system information. No further data need be sent in the registers, and the results are returned via the

151

registers. D1 will contain the current job ID, important data when timesharing is going on. D2 will hold an ASCII representation of which version of QDOS is the machine's ROM. A0 on return points to the base of the system variables area (provision for moving the SVs gives the possibility of using the second screen). The codes to try this, using the monitor program, are: MOVEQ #0,D0 (70000h), TRAP 1 (4E41h), MOVEM D0–A7, address (48F9h, FFFFh, long word address of area to store registers), RTS (4E75h). If you load this code into free space and run it, the contents of the registers will be dumped in memory, starting at the location given by the address. You can then look at the results. You will find that the job ID will be zero and the ASCII version will be at least 1.01.

The next group of routines available from trap 1 deals with jobs in the transient program area (D0 = 1 to Bh). These are user machine code programs that are capable of being run concurrently. Trap 1 with 0Ch or 0Dh loaded into D0 invokes routines to set up or delete areas in the user heap.

Trap 1 with D0 set to 0Eh will allocate space in the resident procedure area. D1 needs to be loaded with the size of the space required. On return, A0 will point to the first address of the area allocated: this trap is the simplest way of reserving space; it works in the same manner as RESPR. Trap 1 with D0=0Fh is meant to release the resident procedure area, but the transient program area needs to be empty.

The display modes can be monitored or reset with trap 1, D0=10h: the two parameters are sent in D1 and D2. If these are passed as −1 (ie MOVEQ #FF,D1 and D2), then the routine reads the mode and display type and returns them in D1 and D2 respectively. Regarding the mode, 0 represents 512 (four-colour) and 8 stands for 256 (eight-colour). To change the display, these values should be passed in the registers.

By loading D0 with 11h and calling trap 1, we can send a command to the IPC. The command consists of a string of bytes in memory, and, in order to inform the trap software of the whereabouts of the string, we must load A3 with the first address before we call the trap. The string has the following format: the first byte is the link command; next is a length byte, followed by a long word that is used as a mask; extra bytes of data follow and finally a terminating byte is required. The link command has a value of 0 to 0Fh: 0 resets the system; 1 reports the input status; 2 to 7 are RS232 commands; 8 reads the keyboard; 9 works in the same manner as the SuperBASIC function KEYROW; 0Ah starts the sound; 0Bh stops it; 0Ch affects the microdrive sensitivity; 0Dh changes the baud rate; 0Eh returns a random number; and 0Fh tests the system. The next byte of the command string holds the number of extra bytes of data that are to be read into the IPC. The mask holds a binary pattern, using two bits for each byte, the least significant referring to the first extra byte. If the LSB is set, then the whole of the extra byte is ignored: if the next bit is not set, then only the low nibble of the byte is passed on to the IPC. Therefore, a mask of 00000000h would mean that only the low nibbles are passed on, while a mask of AAAAAAAh would ensure that all the data was transferred.

Let us look at the commands which we may need to use. 09h words like KEYROW: the following string of bytes will activate a scanning operation — 09, 01, 00, 00, 00, 00, 'row', 02, where 'row' is the number of the row we wish to scan. The result of the scan will be returned in D1.

To generate a simple tone, use the following command string — 0A, 08, AAAAAAAA, 'pitch', 00, 00, 00, 'dur low', 'dur high', 00, 00, where the two 'dur' (duration) parameters are stored LSB first. The zeros consist of the other beep parameters. The last byte, for example, introduces randomness.

To stop sound, 0B, 00 will suffice. No extra bytes are needed to return a four-bit random number with command 0E.

Of the remaining trap 1 calls, D0=12h sets the baud rate to that passed in D1; D0=13h to 15h reads, sets and adjusts the clock, using D1 to pass parameters; and the rest are memory management and interrupt system calls.

Trap 2
Trap 2 has only three calls: these open and close channels and format microdrives.

Trap 3
Trap 3 handles input and output. There are over 60 variations of this trap, so I will only look at the few simple ones that you may wish to use from within your own machine code programs. With D0 set to 1, trap 3 fetches a byte from a channel: if the channel is linked to the keyboard it will return the ASCII code of the first key pressed in D1. All the trap 3 calls require the channel number to be held in A0, and this must be a long word with the channel number in both words. For example, using channel 1 would require A0 to be loaded with 00010001h. Register D3 needs to be loaded with a timeout — that is to say, you can determine how long you will wait for a keypress (or whatever operation is being performed). By loading D3 with −1 (FFFFFFFFh), the routine will wait for ever. To fetch a keypress using this trap try the following:

```
MOVEQ   #1,D0     (7001)
MOVEQ   #FF,D3    (76FF)
LEA     0,A0      (41F9,0,0)
```

TRAP   #3   (4E43)
RTS   (4E75)

On return, D1 will hold the code of the keypress. You may fetch a string of bytes that terminate with an 'LF' (the return key) by using D0=2: you must set up a buffer area of RAM by pointing A1 to a free space and loading D2 with the size of the buffer. The string that is typed in (and ends with a RETURN) will be found in the buffer area after the trap. D0 set to 3 performs much the same function but does not stop once a RETURN is fetched: it waits until the buffer is full.

Sending bytes is just as simple. To send a single byte, load it into D1, put a timeout of −1 in D3, a channel ID in A0 and 5 in D0: now call trap 3 and the task is performed! To send a string, load D0 with 7, D2 with the number of bytes to send, D3 with a timeout, A0 with the channel ID and point A1 at the bytes (stored in a buffer).

In conjunction with sending characters to the screen, you may wish to alter the cursor position. With timeout and channel ID as normal, D0=10h sets the cursor to the row position held in D1 and column position in D2. D0=11h tabulates the column only, D0=12h forces a newline, and D0=13h to 16h act as do the cursor keys, moving the cursor left, right, down and up respectively.

Scrolling can be achieved with D0=18h (whole window), D0=19h (above cursor line) or D0=1Ah (below cursor line). The distance of the scroll should be loaded into D1: a negative distance scrolls the screen up. Panning follows the same format, using the D0 values 1Bh, 1Eh and 1Fh, which pan the whole window, the cursor line or the righthand end of the cursor line. A negative pan moves the screen image left.

Clearing a window is possible. You may clear the whole window (D0=20h), above the cursor (D0=21h), below the cursor (D0=22h), the cursor line itself (D0=23h), or the righthand end of the cursor line (D0=24h). Resetting the fount (D0=25h) was described in Chapter 10.

The final trap 3 command I will mention resets the colours. The new colour should be placed in D1. D0=27h alters the paper, 28h the strip and 29h the ink colours.

Vectors

Earlier, I mentioned that some QDOS calls did not use the trap mechanism. The vector addresses C0h upwards contain the addresses of some useful calls. One that may be of interest is stored at D0: it sends a message to a channel and is more compact than the equivalent trap. The message needs to be stored in RAM, and the first word holds the length of the message. A0 should be pointed at the message. Try the following routine, loading it with the monitor program:

```
LEA          10001,A0      41F9,1,1
LEA          0C,(PC),A2    43FA,C
SUBA.L       A2,A2         95CA
MOVEA.W      D0,A2         3478,D0
JSR          (A2)          4E92
RTS                        4E75
Data                       000A, 4120, 4D65, 7373, 6167, 652E
```

The information I have provided on the operating system will allow you to write many machine code programs: using QDOS to the full will require complete documentation, which Sinclair promises to publish.

We have now reached the point where all the major aspects of the QL have been explained: how you use this knowledge will depend on how you use your computer. Some people drive a car with no desire to open the bonnet; others prefer to have some idea of how it works even if they don't ever intend getting their hands dirty. If you see yourself as a potential computer 'mechanic', then you will need to acquire machine code skills, as well as exercising a great deal of patience. You will find many more books published on the finer points of the QL: as for books about patience. . . .

Other titles from Sunshine

SPECTRUM BOOKS

Artificial Intelligence on the Spectrum Computer
Keith & Steven Brain   ISBN 0 946408 37 8   **£6.95**

Spectrum Adventures
Tony Bridge & Roy Carnell   ISBN 0 946408 07 6   **£5.95**

Machine Code Sprites and Graphics for the ZX Spectrum
John Durst   ISBN 0 946408 51 3   **£6.95**

ZX Spectrum Astronomy
Maurice Gavin   ISBN 0 946408 24 6   **£6.95**

Spectrum Machine Code Applications
David Laine   ISBN 0 946408 17 3   **£6.95**

The Working Spectrum
David Lawrence   ISBN 0 946408 00 9   **£5.95**

Inside your Spectrum
Jeff Naylor & Diane Rogers   ISBN 0 946408 35 1   **£6.95**

Master your ZX Microdrive
Andrew Pennell   ISBN 0 946408 19 X   **£6.95**

COMMODORE 64 BOOKS

Graphic Art for the Commodore 64
Boris Allan   ISBN 0 946408 15 7   **£5.95**

Building with LOGO on the Commodore 64
Boris Allan   ISBN 0 946408 48 3   **£6.95**

DIY Robotics and Sensors on the Commodore Computer
John Billingsley   ISBN 0 946408 30 0   **£6.95**

Artificial Intelligence on the Commodore 64
Keith & Steven Brain   ISBN 0 946408 29 7   **£6.95**

Simulation Techniques on the Commodore 64
John Cochrane   ISBN 0 946408 58 0   **£6.95**

Machine Code Graphics and Sound for the Commodore 64
Mark England & David Lawrence   ISBN 0 946408 28 9   **£6.95**

Commodore 64 Adventures
Mike Grace   ISBN 0 946408 11 4   **£5.95**

Business Applications for the Commodore 64
James Hall   ISBN 0 946408 12 2   **£5.95**

Electronic Music on the Commodore 64
Mark Jenkins   ISBN 0 946408 59 9   **£6.95**

156

Mathematics on the Commodore 64
Czes Kosniowski   ISBN 0 946408 14 9   **£5.95**

Advanced Programming Techniques on the Commodore 64
David Lawrence   ISBN 0 946408 23 8   **£5.95**

Commodore 64 Disk Companion
David Lawrence & Mark England   ISBN 0 946408 49 1   **£7.95**

The Working Commodore 64
David Lawrence   ISBN 0 946408 02 5   **£5.95**

Commodore 64 Machine Code Master
David Lawrence & Mark England   ISBN 0 946408 05 X   **£6.95**

Machine Code Games Routines for the Commodore 64
Paul Roper   ISBN 0 946408 47 5   **£6.95**

Programming for Education on the Commodore 64
John Scriven & Patrick Hall   ISBN 0 946408 27 0   **£5.95**

Commodore 64 Music
Ian Waugh   ISBN 0 946408 78 5   **£6.95**

Writing Strategy Games on your Commodore 64
John White   ISBN 0 946408 54 8   **£6.95**

COMMODORE 16/PLUS 4 BOOKS

The Working C16
David Lawrence   ISBN 0 946408 62 9   **£6.95**

The Commodore C16/Plus 4 Companion
Brian Lloyd   ISBN 0 946408 64 5   **£5.95**

ELECTRON BOOKS

Graphic Art for the Electron Computer
Boris Allan   ISBN 0 946408 20 3   **£5.95**

The Working Electron
John Scriven   ISBN 0 946408 52 1   **£5.95**

Programming for Education on the Electron Computer
John Scriven & Patrick Hall   ISBN 0 946408 21 1   **£5.95**

BBC COMPUTER BOOKS

Functional Forth for the BBC Computer
Boris Allan   ISBN 0 946408 04 1   **£5.95**

Graphic Art for the BBC Computer
Boris Allan   ISBN 0 946408 08 4   **£5.95**

DIY Robotics and Sensors for the BBC Computer
John Billingsley   ISBN 0 946408 13 0   **£6.95**
Artificial Intelligence on the BBC/Electron
Keith & Steven Brain   ISBN 0 946408 36 X   **£6.95**
Essential Maths on the BBC and Electron Computer
Czes Kosniowski   ISBN 0 946408 34 3   **£5.95**
Programming for Education on the BBC Computer
John Scriven & Patrick Hall   ISBN 0 946408 10 6   **£5.95**
Making Music on the BBC Computer
Ian Waugh   ISBN 0 946408 26 2   **£5.95**

DRAGON BOOKS

Advanced Sound & Graphics for the Dragon
Keith & Steven Brain   ISBN 0 946408 06 8   **£5.95**
Artificial Intelligence on the Dragon Computer
Keith & Steven Brain   ISBN 0 946408 33 5   **£6.95**
Dragon 32 Games Master
Keith & Steven Brain   ISBN 0 946408 03 3   **£5.95**
The Working Dragon
David Lawrence   ISBN 0 946408 01 7   **£5.95**
The Dragon Trainer
Brian Lloyd   ISBN 0 946408 09 2   **£5.95**

ATARI BOOKS

Atari Adventures
Tony Bridge   ISBN 0 946408 18 1   **£5.95**
Writing Strategy Games on your Atari Computer
John White   ISBN 0 946408 22 X   **£5.95**

SINCLAIR QL BOOKS

Artificial Intelligence on the Sinclair QL
Keith & Steven Brain   ISBN 0 946408 41 6   **£6.95**
Sinclair QL Adventures
Tony Bridge & Richard Williams   ISBN 0 946408 66 1   **£5.95**
Introduction to Simulation Techniques on the Sinclair QL
John Cochrane   ISBN 0 946408 45 9   **£6.95**
Developing Applications for the Sinclair QL
Mike Grace   ISBN 0 946408 63 7   **£6.95**

Mathematics on the Sinclair QL
Czes Kosniowski   ISBN 0 946408 43 2   **£6.95**

The Working Sinclair QL
David Lawrence   ISBN 0 946408 46 7   **£6.95**

Quill, Easel, Archive & Abacus on the Sinclair QL
Alison McCallum-Varey   ISBN 0 946408 55 6   **£6.95**

Inside the Sinclair QL
Jeff Naylor & Diane Rogers   ISBN 0 946408 40 8   **£6.95**

Assembly Language Programming on the Sinclair QL
Andrew Pennell   ISBN 0 946408 42 4   **£7.95**

AMSTRAD BOOKS

The Working Amstrad
David Lawrence & Simon Lane   ISBN 0 946408 60 2   **£5.95**

GENERAL BOOKS

Home Applications on your Micro
Mike Grace   ISBN 0 946408 50 5   **£6.95**

Sunshine also publishes

POPULAR COMPUTING WEEKLY

The first weekly magazine for home computer users. Each copy contains Top 10 charts of the best-selling software and books and up-to-the-minute details of the latest games. Other features in the magazine include regular hardware and software reviews, programming hints, computer swap, adventure corner and pages of listings for the Spectrum, Dragon, BBC, VIC 20 and 64, ZX 81 and other popular micros. Only 40p a week, a year's subscription costs £19.95 (£9.98 for six months) in the UK and £37.40 (£18.70 for six months) overseas.

DRAGON USER

The monthly magazine for all users of Dragon microcomputers. Each issue contains reviews of software and peripherals, programming advice for beginners and advanced users, program listings, a technical advisory service and all the latest news related to the Dragon. A year's subscription (12 issues) costs £10 in the UK and £16 overseas.

COMMODORE HORIZONS

The monthly magazine for all users of Commodore computers. Each issue contains reviews of software and peripherals, programming advice for beginners and advanced users, program listings, a technical advisory service and all the latest news. A year's subscription costs £10 in the UK and £16 overseas.

For further information contact:
Sunshine
12–13 Little Newport Street
London WC2H 7PP
01-437 4343

Telex: 296275